Power Maths

Year 4
Practice Book 4E

GW00420422

White Rose Ma...

Draw your favourite food.

How would you share it equally between your friends.

This book belongs to _____ .

My class is _____ .

Series editor: Tony Staneff

Lead author: Josh Lury

Consultants (first edition): Professor Liu Jian and Professor Zhang Dan

Author team (first edition): Tony Staneff, Josh Lury, Belle Cottingham, Jonathan East, Caroline Hamilton, Rebecca Holland, Stephen Monaghan, and Paul Wrangles

Pearson

Contents

This looks like a good challenge!

It's time to do some practice!

3

How to use this book

Do you remember how to use this **Practice Book**?

Use the **Textbook** first to learn how to solve this type of problem.

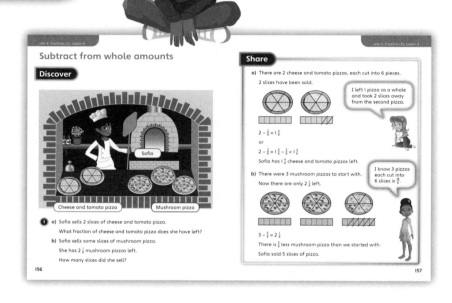

This shows you which **Textbook** page you need.

Have a go at questions by yourself using this **Practice Book**. Use what you have learnt.

Challenge questions make you think hard!

Questions with this light bulb make you think differently.

Reflect

Each lesson ends with a **Reflect** question so you can think about what you have learnt.

Use **My power points** at the back of this book to keep track of what you have learnt.

My journal

At the end of a unit your teacher will ask you to fill in **My journal**.

This will help you show how much you can do now that you have finished the unit.

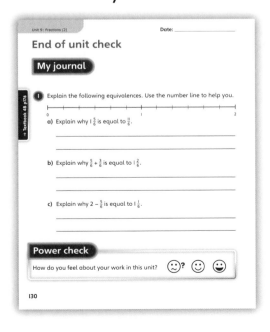

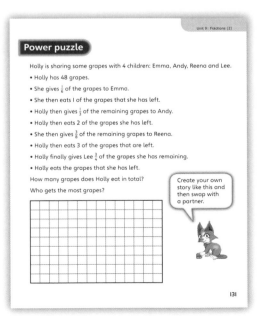

Date: _____

↑ Textbook 4B p8

Factor pairs

① Write the factor pairs for the number 10.

a)

$$\boxed{} \times \boxed{} = 10$$

$$\boxed{} \times \boxed{} = 10$$

b)

$$\boxed{} \times \boxed{} = 10$$

$$\boxed{} \times \boxed{} = 10$$

② Write the factor pairs for the number 14.

a)

$$\boxed{} \times \boxed{} = 14$$

$$\boxed{} \times \boxed{} = 14$$

b)

$$\boxed{} \times \boxed{} = 14$$

$$\boxed{} \times \boxed{} = 14$$

③ Write the factor pairs for the number 15.

$$\boxed{} \times \boxed{} = 15 \qquad \boxed{} \times \boxed{} = 15$$

$$\boxed{} \times \boxed{} = 15 \qquad \boxed{} \times \boxed{} = 15$$

4 Find all the factor pairs for the number 36.

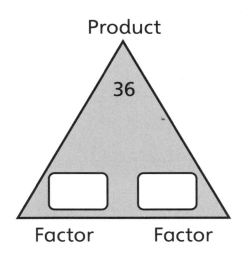

Product

36

Factor   Factor

5 Do you agree with Olivia? Explain your answer.

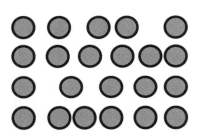

This shows 4 is a factor of 22, because there are 4 rows.

Olivia

_____

_____

6 Write down all the factor pairs of

a) 24 _____

b) 18 _____

c) 25 _____

7

7 Find all the factor pairs for the number 100.

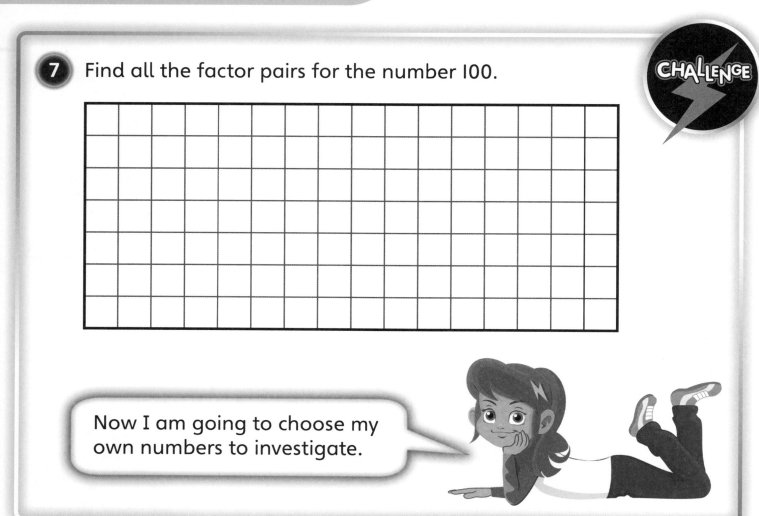

CHALLENGE

Now I am going to choose my own numbers to investigate.

Reflect

Which of these numbers has a factor of 2?

Discuss with a partner how you know.

| 30 | 31 | 32 | 33 | 34 | 35 |

Date: _____

Multiply and divide by 10

1 Complete the calculations.

a) $5 \times 10 =$ ☐

b) $15 \times 10 =$ ☐

c) $35 \times 10 =$ ☐

d) ☐ $\times 10 = 650$

e) $90 \div 10 =$ ☐

f) $190 \div 10 =$ ☐

g) $490 \div 10 =$ ☐

h) ☐ $\div 10 = 99$

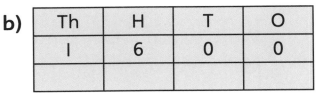

2 Multiply each number by 10. Write it in the place value grid.

a)

Th	H	T	O
		1	8

c)

Th	H	T	O
		3	5

b)

Th	H	T	O
	3	1	8

d)

Th	H	T	O
	1	0	3

3 Divide each number by 10. Write it in the place value grid.

a)

Th	H	T	O
	4	5	0

b)

Th	H	T	O
1	6	0	0

→ Textbook 4B p12

4 Find the missing numbers.

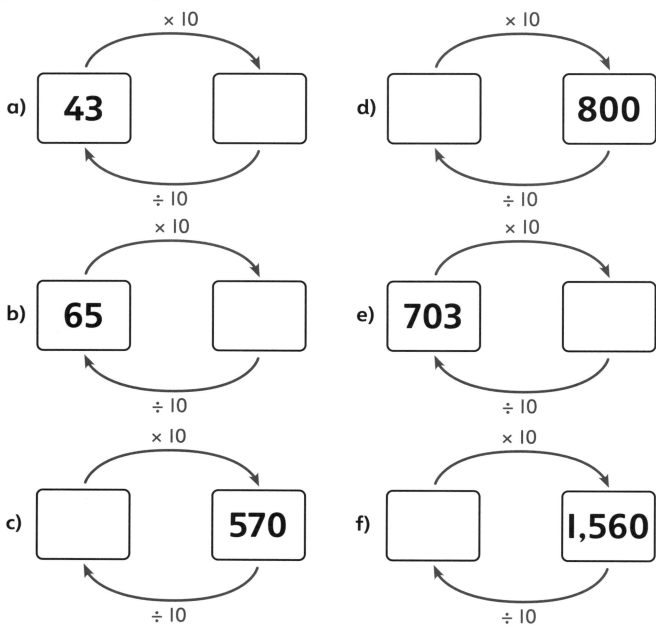

a) × 10 : 43 → [ ] ÷ 10

b) × 10 : 65 → [ ] ÷ 10

c) × 10 : [ ] → 570 ÷ 10

d) × 10 : [ ] → 800 ÷ 10

e) × 10 : 703 → [ ] ÷ 10

f) × 10 : [ ] → 1,560 ÷ 10

5 Complete the product factor triangle.

Write four number sentences for the fact family.

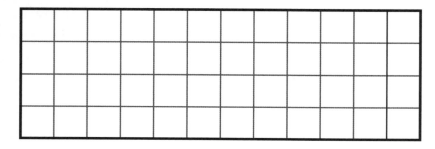

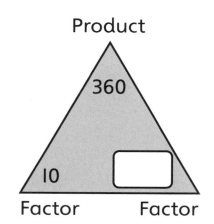

Product

360

10   [ ]

Factor   Factor

6 Complete

a) 130 × 10 = ☐

b) ☐ × 10 = 7,900

c) ☐ × 10 = 6,050

d) ☐ ÷ 10 = 45

e) ☐ ÷ 10 = 530

f) 7,530 ÷ 10 = ☐

CHALLENGE

7 a) A worm is 12 cm long.

A snake is 10 times as long as the worm.

What is the length of the snake? ☐

b) Write your own story for

25 × 10 = 250

_____

_____

_____

Reflect

Tell a partner what happens when you multiply a number by 10.

Date: _____

↑ Textbook 4B p16

Multiply and divide by 100

1 Complete the calculations.

a) $7 \times 100 = $ ⬚

b) $17 \times 100 = $ ⬚

c) $37 \times 100 = $ ⬚

d) ⬚ $\times 100 = 6{,}700$

e) $6{,}600 \div 100 = $ ⬚

f) $6{,}700 \div 100 = $ ⬚

g) $6{,}800 \div 100 = $ ⬚

h) ⬚ $\div 100 = 7{,}000$

2 Multiply each number by 100. Write it in the place value grid.

a)

Th	H	T	O
			8

c)

Th	H	T	O
		6	0

b)

Th	H	T	O
		2	6

d)

Th	H	T	O
		9	3

3 Divide each number by 100. Write it in the place value grid.

a)

Th	H	T	O
9	4	0	0

b)

Th	H	T	O
4	0	0	0

Find the missing numbers.

a)

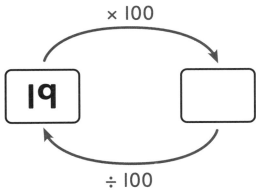

× 100

19

÷ 100

d)

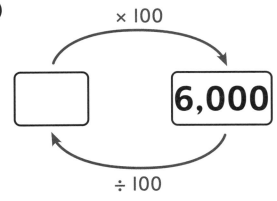

× 100

6,000

÷ 100

b)

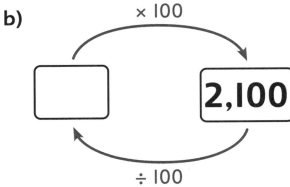

× 100

2,100

÷ 100

e)

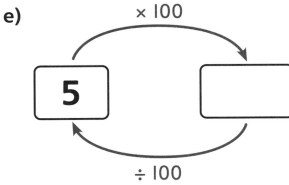

× 100

5

÷ 100

c)

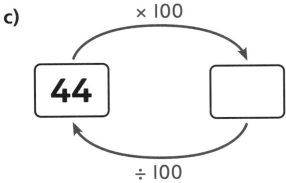

× 100

44

÷ 100

f)

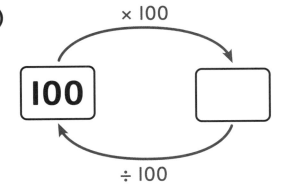

× 100

100

÷ 100

5 Complete the product factor triangle.

Write four number sentences for the fact family.

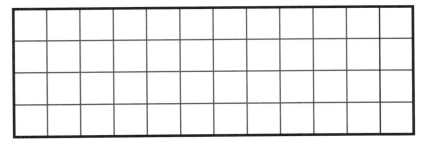

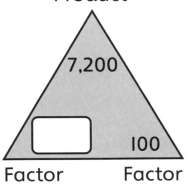

Product

7,200

100

Factor   Factor

6 Write the length of each animal in cm.

CHALLENGE

I m is 100 cm.

a)

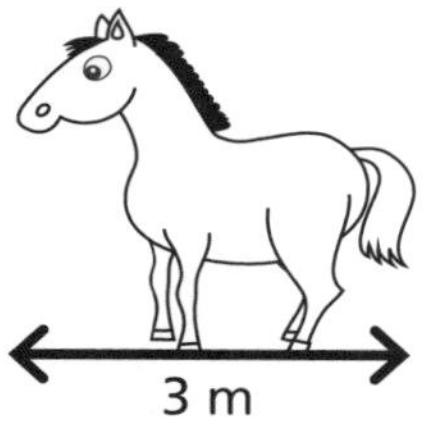

[ ] cm

3 m

b)

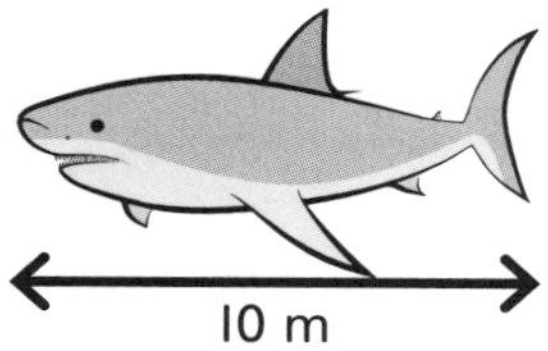

[ ] cm

10 m

c)

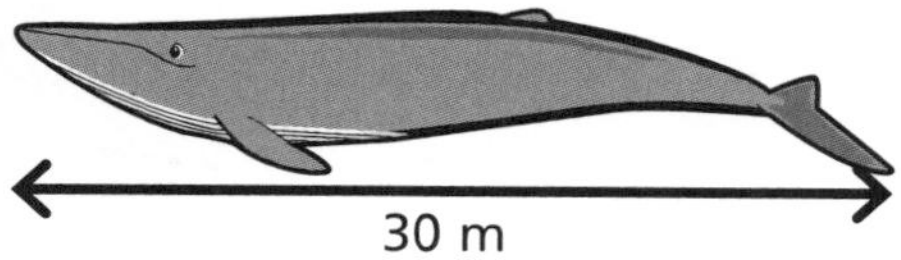

[ ] cm

30 m

Reflect

Work with a partner.

Describe everything you know about multiplying and dividing by 10 and 100.

Related facts – multiplication

① Complete the multiplications.

a)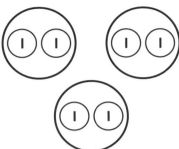

$3 \times 2 = \boxed{}$

b)

$3 \times 20 = \boxed{}$

c)

$3 \times 200 = \boxed{}$

② Complete the multiplications.

a)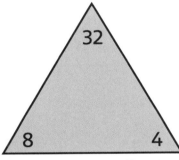

Product
32
8   4
Factor   Factor

$8 \times 40 = \boxed{}$

$8 \times 400 = \boxed{}$

$80 \times 4 = \boxed{}$

$800 \times 4 = \boxed{}$

b)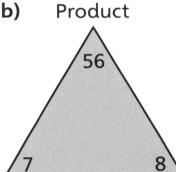

Product
56
7   8
Factor   Factor

$70 \times 8 = \boxed{}$

$80 \times 7 = \boxed{}$

$7 \times 800 = \boxed{}$

$8 \times 700 = \boxed{}$

c)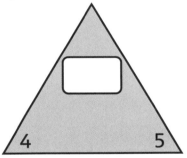

Product
$\boxed{}$
4   5
Factor   Factor

$5 \times 40 = \boxed{}$

$500 \times 4 = \boxed{}$

$400 \times 5 = \boxed{}$

$5 \times 50 = \boxed{}$

3 Complete these calculations.

a) $7 \times 4 =$ ☐

$7 \times 40 =$ ☐

$7 \times 400 =$ ☐

b) $8 \times 80 =$ ☐

$8 \times 30 =$ ☐

$3 \times 8 =$ ☐

c) $9 \times 2 =$ ☐

$9 \times 20 =$ ☐

$200 \times 9 =$ ☐

d) $9 \times 50 =$ ☐

$80 \times 9 =$ ☐

$600 \times 4 =$ ☐

4 Complete the multiplication shown on the number line.

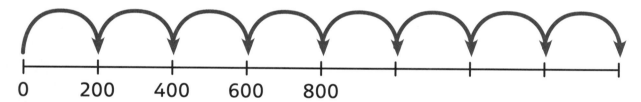

0   200   400   600   800

☐ × ☐ = ☐

5 What is the total mass?

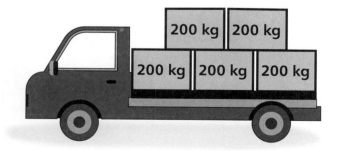

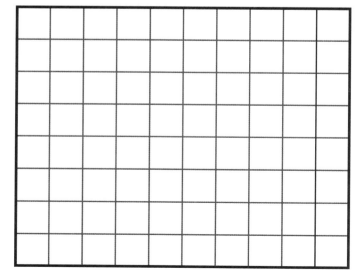

Mass = ☐ kg

6 Work out 7 × 30 using three different methods.

Method I

7 × 30 =

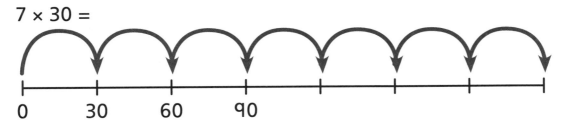

Method 2

7 × 3 ones = ☐ ones = ☐

So, 7 × 3 tens = ☐ tens = ☐

Method 3

7 × 3 = ☐   So, ☐ × I0 = ☐

Tell a partner which method you prefer.

Reflect

Choose one of these calculations and explain how you can use 7 × 4 = 28 to work it out.

| 7 × 40 | 70 × 4 | 700 × 4 | 7 × 400 |

_____

_____

_____

Date: _____

Related facts – division

1 Complete the divisions.

a)

$6 \div 2 = \boxed{}$

b) (10) (10) (10) (10) (10) (10)

$60 \div 2 = \boxed{}$

c) (100) (100) (100) (100) (100) (100)

$600 \div 2 = \boxed{}$

2 Complete the divisions.

a)　　$15 \div 3 = 5$

　　$150 \div 3 = \boxed{}$

　　$1{,}500 \div 3 = \boxed{}$

b)　　$15 \div 5 = \boxed{}$

　　$150 \div 5 = \boxed{}$

　　$1{,}500 \div 5 = \boxed{}$

c)　　$21 \div 3 = 7$

　　$210 \div 3 = \boxed{}$

　　$2{,}100 \div 3 = \boxed{}$

d)　　$25 \div 5 = \boxed{}$

　　$250 \div 5 = \boxed{}$

　　$2{,}500 \div 5 = \boxed{}$

e)　　$24 \div 3 = \boxed{}$

　　$240 \div 3 = \boxed{}$

　　$2{,}400 \div 3 = \boxed{}$

f)　　$45 \div 5 = \boxed{}$

　　$450 \div 5 = \boxed{}$

　　$4{,}500 \div 5 = \boxed{}$

3 Draw lines from each calculation to the correct answer.

| 400 ÷ 5 |

| 480 ÷ 6 |

| 40 ÷ 5 |

| 32 ÷ 4 |

| 32 tens ÷ 4 |

| 8 |

| 80 |

| 800 |

| 1,600 ÷ 2 |

| 4 thousands ÷ 5 |

| 720 ÷ 9 |

| 800 ÷ 10 |

4 Complete the calculations.

a) $4 \times \boxed{} = 3{,}600$

b) $40 \times \boxed{} = 3{,}600$

c) $400 \times \boxed{} = 3{,}600$

d) $\boxed{} \div 9 = 400$

e) $\boxed{} \div 4 = 900$

f) $\boxed{} \div 4 = 90$

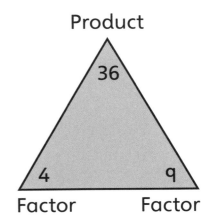

Product

36

4   9

Factor   Factor

5) Here is a function machine.

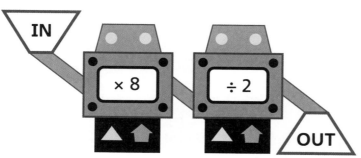

Complete the table.

IN	6	60	600	20	300		
OUT						40	120

What do you notice?

_____

_____

Reflect

Explain how to divide 1,200 by 4 and discuss it with a partner.

Did your partner use the same method?

_____

_____

_____

Multiply and add

1 What is the score of the shaded dice?

What is the score of the white dice?

What is the total score?

→ Textbook 4B p28

a)

$5 \times 2 = \boxed{}$ $2 \times 2 = \boxed{}$ $7 \times 2 = \boxed{}$

b)

$5 \times 4 = \boxed{}$ $2 \times 4 = \boxed{}$ $7 \times 4 = \boxed{}$

c)

$5 \times 6 = \boxed{}$ $3 \times 6 = \boxed{}$ $8 \times 6 = \boxed{}$

d)

$5 \times 6 = \boxed{}$ $4 \times 6 = \boxed{}$ $9 \times 6 = \boxed{}$

e)

$5 \times 5 = \boxed{}$ $4 \times 5 = \boxed{}$ $9 \times 5 = \boxed{}$

2 Complete the calculations.

a) 7 × 8 = ☐

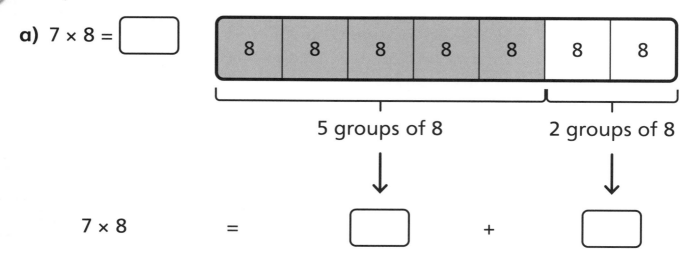

7 × 8 = ☐ + ☐

b) 9 × 8 = ☐

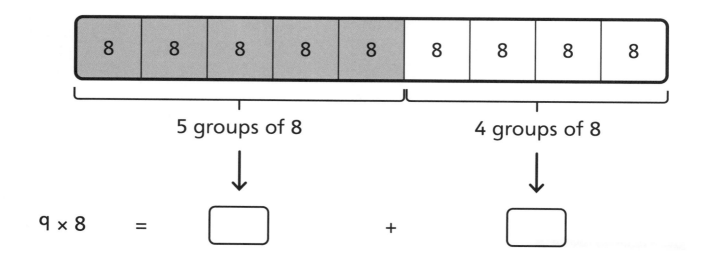

9 × 8 = ☐ + ☐

3 Use the bar model to calculate 9 × 4.

| 4 | 4 | 4 | 4 | 4 | 4 | 4 | 4 | 4 |

9 × 4 = ☐

4 Complete the number sentences.

a) $4 \times 6 + 3 \times 6 = \boxed{} \times 6$

b) $7 \times 5 + 3 \times 5 = \boxed{} \times 5$

c) $9 \times 4 + \boxed{} \times 4 = 11 \times 4$

d) $5 \times 2 + 1 \times 2 = \boxed{} \times 2$

e) $4 \times 2 + 2 \times 5 = \boxed{} \times 2$

f) $\boxed{} \times 3 + 5 \times 3 = 9 \times 3$

5 Explain the method you would use to work out the total number of counters.

First I would _____

_____ .

Then I would _____

_____ .

There are $\boxed{}$ counters in total.

Reflect

Explain why $5 \times 3 + 2 \times 3$ is the same as 7×3.

_____

_____

_____

Date: _____

Informal written methods

1 How many eggs are there in total?

a)

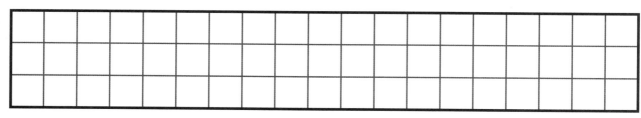

b)

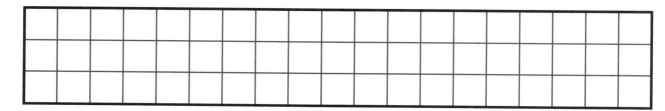

2 Complete each calculation.

a)

10 × 3	6 × 3

$16 \times 3 = \boxed{} + \boxed{}$

$= \boxed{}$

b)

10 × 8	3 × 8

$13 \times 8 = \boxed{} + \boxed{}$

$= \boxed{}$

3 Complete the multiplication facts.

a) 10 × 5 = ☐

7 × 5 = ☐

17 × 5 = ☐

b) 4 × 10 = ☐

4 × 6 = ☐

4 × 16 = ☐

c) 3 × 6 = ☐

20 × 6 = ☐

23 × 6 = ☐

d) 3 × 40 = ☐

3 × 5 = ☐

3 × 45 = ☐

e) 20 × 8 = ☐

5 × 8 = ☐

25 × 8 = ☐

f) 11 × 7 = ☐

5 × 7 = ☐

16 × 7 = ☐

4 Complete each calculation.

a) 15 × 3 = ☐

b) 21 × 6 = ☐

c) 18 × 5 = ☐

d) 5 × 51 = ☐

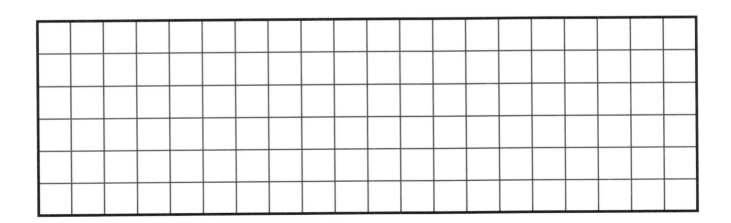

5 Solve each calculation.

a) 37 × 3 = ☐

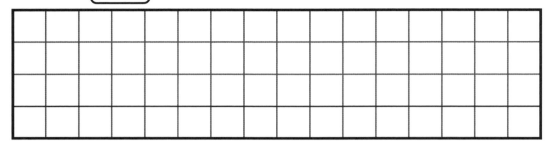

b) 77 × 3 = ☐

Reflect

Discuss how you could work out the total number of pencils.

Multiply 2 digits by 1 digit

1 The place value counters show a multiplication.

Complete the multiplication and then find the answer.

	H	T	O	
		4	1	
×			5	

2 Fill in the missing numbers.

a)

	H	T	O	
		5	3	
×			6	

c)

	H	T	O	
		2	9	
×			4	

b)

	H	T	O	
		4	7	
×			3	

d)

	H	T	O	
		2	2	
×			8	

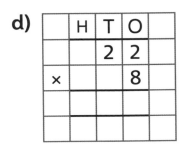

I am going to use counters to check my answers.

3 Work out the answers to these multiplications.

a) 28 × 5 = ☐

c) 64 × 9 = ☐

b) 37 × 4 = ☐

d) 7 × 32 = ☐

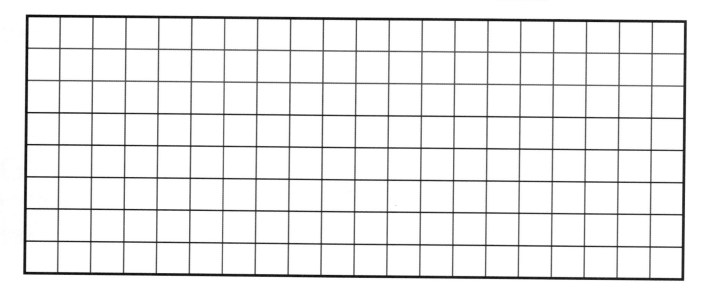

4 Each day Amal travels 54 km to and from work. How many kilometres does he travel in 5 days?

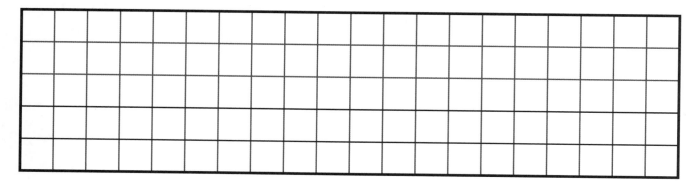

Amal travels ☐ km in 5 days.

5 Lee has made a mistake working out 54 × 6.

	Th	H	T	O
			5	4
×				6
	3	0	2	4

Thinking about place value columns might help me to explain Lee's mistake.

Explain to a partner the mistake Lee has made.

6 Fill in the missing numbers.

CHALLENGE

a)

	H	T	O
	5	7	
×		▢	
1		1	

b)

	H	T	O
		2	▢
×			6
			8

c)

	H	T	O	
		▢	▢	
×			7	
▢	8	3		
	6			

For the first one, I am going to think of a number in the 7 times-table that ends in a 1.

Reflect

Explain to a partner how this diagram matches the calculation.

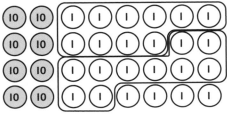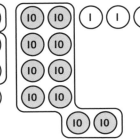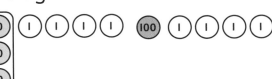

	H	T	O
		2	6
×			4
	1	0	4
		2	

29

Date: _____

Multiply 3 digits by 1 digit

1 The place value counters show a multiplication.

Work out the answer to the multiplication.

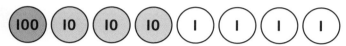

		H	T	O	
		1	3	4	
	×			2	

2 Complete the multiplications.

a)

		H	T	O	
		2	1	3	
	×			4	

b)

		H	T	O	
		1	1	4	
	×			5	

c)

		H	T	O	
		1	1	5	
	×			4	

d)

		H	T	O	
		1	4	8	
	×			3	

e)

		Th	H	T	O	
			2	5	2	
	×				7	

f)

		Th	H	T	O	
			3	1	8	
	×				6	

3 Work out the answers to these multiplications.

a) 122 × 6 = ☐

c) 270 × 3 = ☐

b) 215 × 5 = ☐

d) 4 × 624 = ☐

4 Find the missing numbers.

a)

		Th	H	T	O	
			2	◯	3	
	×				5	
		1	4	6	◯	
					1	

b)

		Th	H	T	O	
			5	1	6	
	×				◯	
		◯	◯	1	2	

5 A bar of soap weighs 145 g.

How much do 8 of these bars weigh?

8 bars of soap weigh ☐ g.

6 Alex is multiplying 136 by 7. What mistakes has she made?

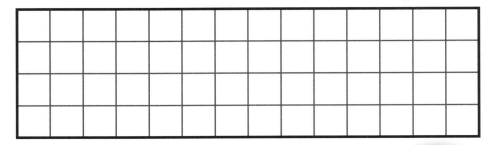

	H	T	O
	1	3	6
×			7
7	25	3	
		4	

7 Here are some digit cards. **1** **2** **5**

CHALLENGE

	Th	H	T	O
		◯	◯	◯
×				7

	Th	H	T	O
		◯	◯	◯
×				7

	Th	H	T	O
		◯	◯	◯
×				7

	Th	H	T	O
		◯	◯	◯
×				7

Arrange the number cards to make these answers:

| 1,505 | 1,064 | 3,584 | 1,757 |

Reflect

Explain to a partner how to multiply 195 by 3.

Can your partner describe a different method?

Solve multiplication problems

→ Textbook 4B p44

1 Emma cuts 7 pieces of ribbon.

Each piece of ribbon is 23 cm long.

How much ribbon does she have?

Emma uses [   ] cm of ribbon.

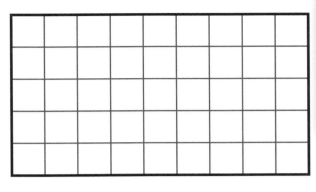

2 The distance from Nottingham to Lancaster is 224 km.

Holly makes this journey 3 times.

a) How many kilometres does Holly travel?

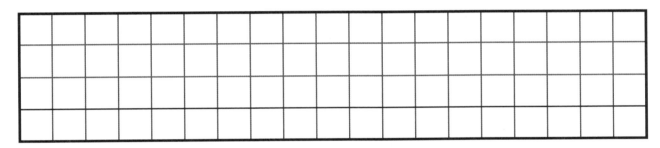

Holly travels [   ] km.

b) It costs Holly 9p per kilometre to drive her car.

How much does it cost in total for the 3 journeys?

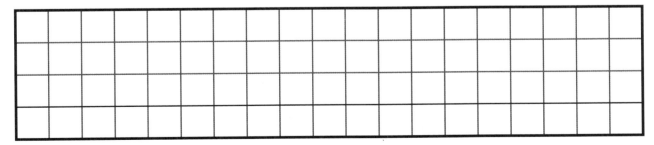

It costs [   ] p in total for the 3 journeys.

3 Andy buys 5 bottles of juice for 79p each and 3 bottles of lemonade for £1 and 19p each.

How much does he spend in total?

?

| 79p | 79p | 79p | 79p | 79p | 119p | 119p | 119p |

Andy spends £ ☐ and ☐ p in total.

4 A cookie weighs 67 g. There are 4 cookies in a box.

Mo buys 6 boxes of cookies.

What is the total weight of the cookies?

The total weight of the cookies is ☐ g.

5 Tower A has 7 cubes, each cube is 86 cm high.

Tower B has 4 cubes, each cube is 1 m 42 cm high.

Which tower is taller?

Remember: 1 m = 100 cm

Tower [   ] is taller.

Reflect

Explain how the bar models help you to solve the following problem.

- Alex cycles 83 km every day of the week.

- Bella cycles 127 km every day except Saturday and Sunday.

What is the difference in the distances they cycle each week?

35

Date: _____

Basic division

1 **a)** Work out $66 \div 3 = \boxed{}$

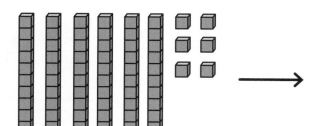

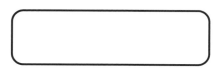

b) Work out $66 \div 6 = \boxed{}$

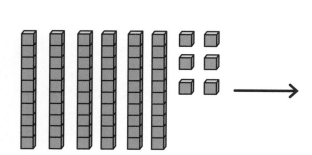

2 Use counters or base 10 equipment to work out these divisions.

a) $64 \div 2 = \boxed{}$

b) $39 \div 3 = \boxed{}$

3 Work out the answers to these divisions.

a) $46 \div 2 =$ [ ]

c) $77 \div 7 =$ [ ]

b) $48 \div 4 =$ [ ]

d) $93 \div 3 =$ [ ]

4 Lexi is working out $84 \div 4$.

Can you spot Lexi's mistake?

What should she have done?

Lexi

I know that
$8 \div 4 = 2$ and $4 \div 4 = 1$,
so I added them
together.

_____

_____

5 Find the answers to these calculations.

a) $40 \div 4 =$ [ ]

b) $63 \div 3 =$ [ ]

$44 \div 4 =$ [ ]

$66 \div 3 =$ [ ]

$48 \div 4 =$ [ ]

$69 \div 3 =$ [ ]

$52 \div 4 =$ [ ]

$72 \div 3 =$ [ ]

6 Explain why 48 ÷ 4 is less than 48 ÷ 2 without working anything out.

CHALLENGE

Use a calculation to check your answer.

_____

_____

_____

_____

Reflect

Explain how you would solve 26 ÷ 2 to someone who does not know how. Use pictures or diagrams to help you.

Date: _____

Division and remainders

1 Use base 10 equipment to help you work out these divisions.

a) $29 \div 2 =$ ☐ r ☐

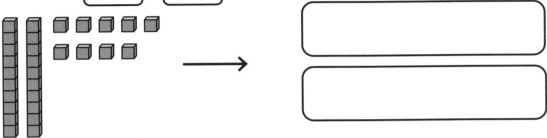

b) $97 \div 3 =$ ☐ r ☐

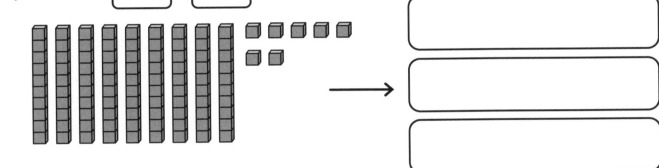

2 What calculation is shown in the diagram?

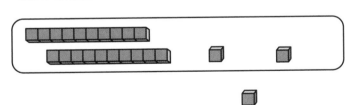

The diagram shows $45 \div$ ☐ $=$ ☐ remainder ☐ .

→ Textbook 4B p52

3 Find the answers to the following calculations.

You can use base 10 equipment or counters to help.

a) 41 ÷ 4 = [   ] r [   ]

b) 59 ÷ 5 = [   ] r [   ]

c) 62 ÷ 3 = [   ] r [   ]

d) 89 ÷ 4 = [   ] r [   ]

e) 62 ÷ 6 = [   ] r [   ]

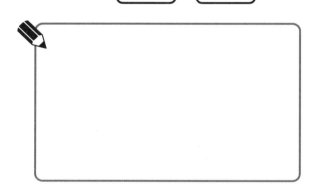

f) 98 ÷ 3 = [   ] r [   ]

4 Using the digit cards 0 to 9, how many division calculations can you make where the answer will have a remainder of 1?

CHALLENGE

◻️◻️ ÷ ◻️ = ◻️ remainder 1

Reflect

Why is there a remainder when you divide 87 by 4?

Use diagrams to support your answer.

Date: _____

Divide 2-digit numbers

1 Use base 10 equipment or counters to work out the divisions.

a) 32 ÷ 2 = ☐

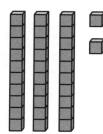

→

☐
☐

b) 42 ÷ 3 = ☐

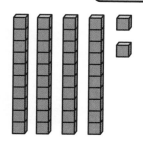

→

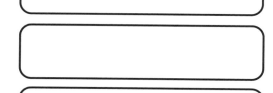

☐
☐

c) 52 ÷ 4 = ☐

→

☐
☐
☐

2 Lexi shares 38 cakes between herself and her friend.

How many cakes do they each get?

They each get ☐ cakes.

42

3 Use drawings, equipment or part-whole models to help you work out the following divisions.

a) $56 \div 4 = \boxed{}$

d) $96 \div 4 = \boxed{}$

b) $45 \div 3 = \boxed{}$

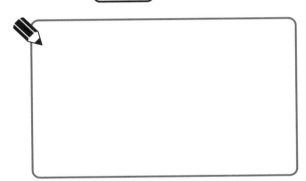

e) $76 \div 2 = \boxed{}$

c) $58 \div 2 = \boxed{}$

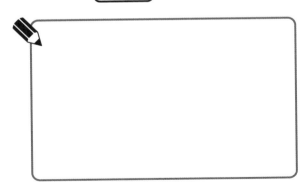

f) $65 \div 5 = \boxed{}$

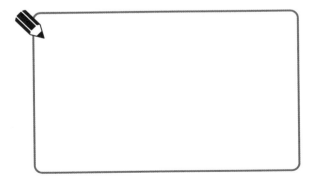

4 Tilly has 75 bulbs. She plants 3 bulbs in each plant pot.

How many plant pots does she need?

Tilly needs ☐ plant pots.

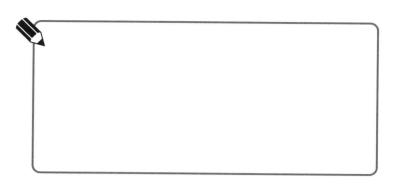

5 **a)** Use the part-whole model to work out

48 ÷ 3 = ☐

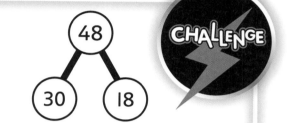

CHALLENGE

b) Use the part-whole model to work out

65 ÷ 5 = ☐

Reflect

Does this partition help you to work out 57 ÷ 3?

What would be a better way to partition 57 to help you?

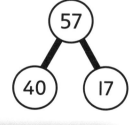

Divide 3-digit numbers

 Work out these calculations. Use drawings or equipment to help you.

a) $188 \div 2 = \boxed{}$

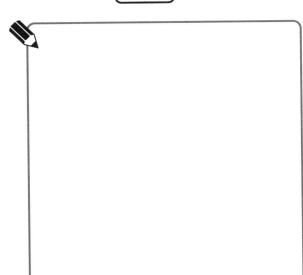

c) $195 \div 5 = \boxed{}$

b) $189 \div 3 = \boxed{}$

d) $275 \div 5 = \boxed{}$

2 Complete the part-whole models and then complete the divisions.

a) 128 ÷ 2 = [   ]

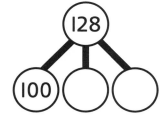

c) 156 ÷ 3 = [   ]

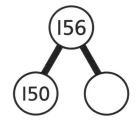

b) 128 ÷ 2 = [   ]

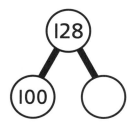

d) 256 ÷ 4 = [   ]

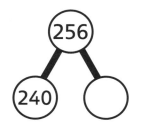

3 Find answers to the following calculations.

a) 185 ÷ 5 = [   ]

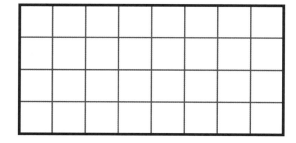

c) 312 ÷ 2 = [   ]

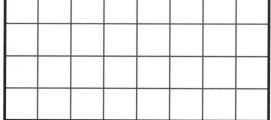

b) 264 ÷ 6 = [   ]

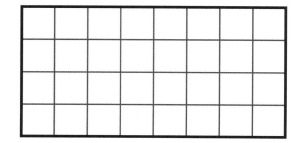

d) 372 ÷ 3 = [   ]

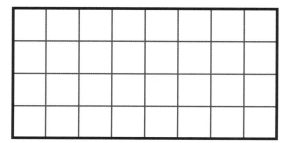

4 What are the division questions shown by these diagrams?

a)
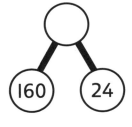

$160 \div 4 = 40$ and $24 \div 4 = 6$

$\boxed{} \div 4 = \boxed{}$

b)
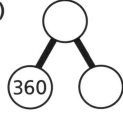

$360 \div 9 = \boxed{}$ and $\boxed{} \div 9 = 3$

$\boxed{} \div 9 = \boxed{}$

5 Show three different partitions that will help you to work out $584 \div 4$.

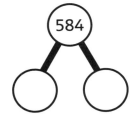
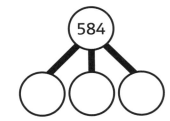
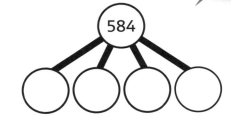

Reflect

Explain how you would work out $172 \div 4$. Why does this method work?

Date: _____

Correspondence problems

↑ Textbook 4B p64

1

a) Draw lines to show how many different ways there are to choose one bucket and one spade.

There are ⬚ different ways to choose one bucket and one spade.

b) What calculation could you use to work this out?

⬚ × ⬚ = ⬚

2 There are 35 different ways that Andy can choose a pair of shorts and a t-shirt.

Andy has 7 pairs of shorts.

How many t-shirts does Andy have?

⬚ × ⬚ = 35

Andy has ⬚ t-shirts.

3 Danny chooses a coin from circle A and a coin from circle B.

Write down all the possible totals of coins he could get.

A 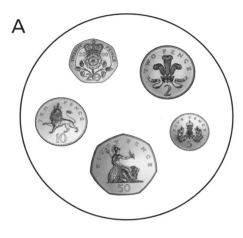 B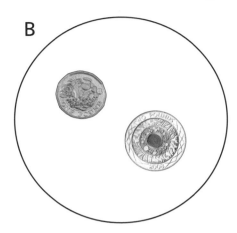

_____

_____

_____

4 Jamilla has some digit cards.

| 1 | 2 | 3 | 4 | 5 | 6 |

a) Show all the possible 2-digit numbers Jamilla could make.

_____

_____

_____

b) Check you have found them all by multiplying.

☐ × ☐ = ☐

☐ different 2-digit numbers can be made.

5 Reena wants to buy two different snacks from the vending machine.

How many different pairs of snacks can she buy?

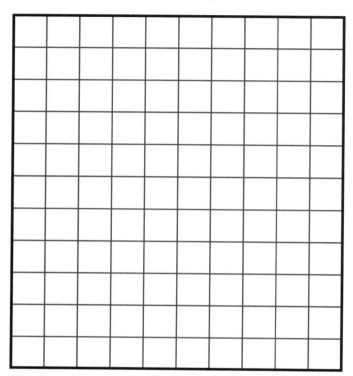

Reflect

How many different ways can you choose a hat and a scarf if you own 5 hats and 3 scarves?

Explain how you got your answer.

Efficient multiplication

1 How many beads are there in total?

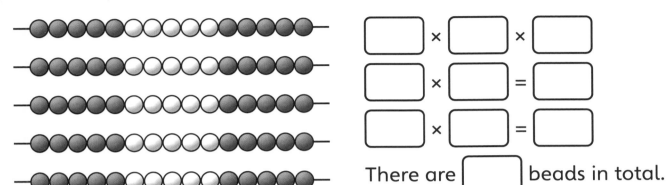

$$\boxed{} \times \boxed{} \times \boxed{}$$

$$\boxed{} \times \boxed{} = \boxed{}$$

$$\boxed{} \times \boxed{} = \boxed{}$$

There are $\boxed{}$ beads in total.

2 How many counters are there in total?

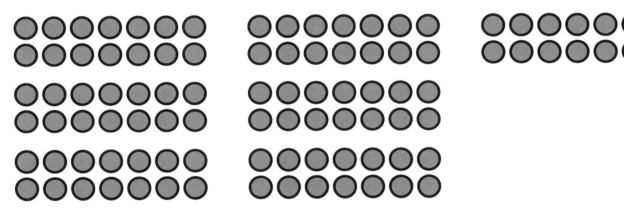

$$\boxed{} \times \boxed{} \times \boxed{} = \boxed{}$$

There are $\boxed{}$ counters in total.

Explain how you worked out how many counters there are in total.

First I _____

_____ .

Then I _____

_____ .

3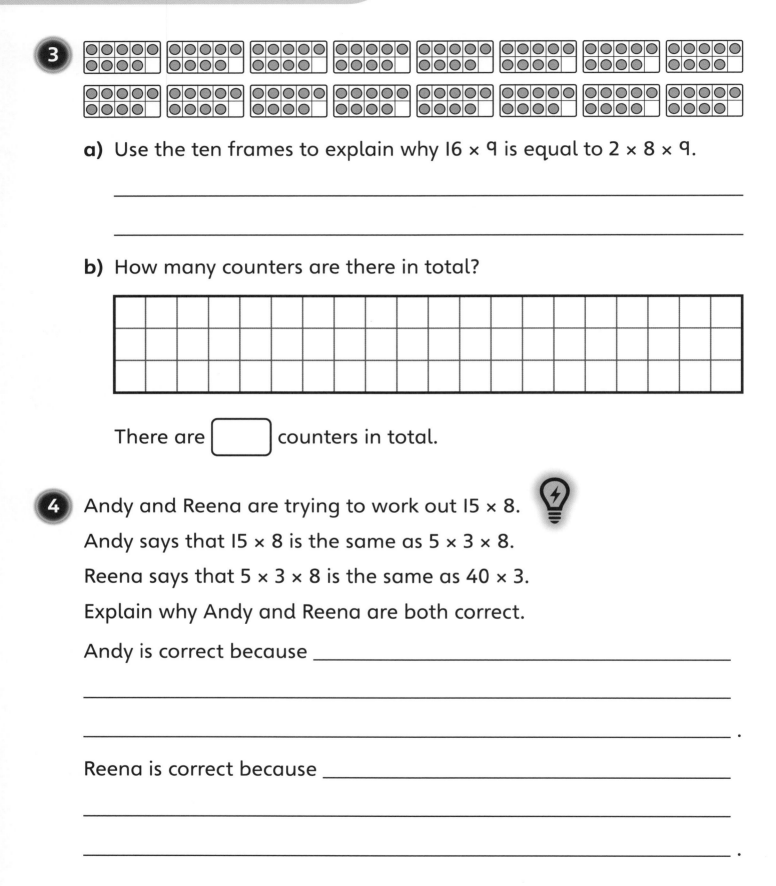

a) Use the ten frames to explain why 16 × 9 is equal to 2 × 8 × 9.

_____

_____

b) How many counters are there in total?

There are ☐ counters in total.

4 Andy and Reena are trying to work out 15 × 8.

Andy says that 15 × 8 is the same as 5 × 3 × 8.

Reena says that 5 × 3 × 8 is the same as 40 × 3.

Explain why Andy and Reena are both correct.

Andy is correct because _____

_____

_____ .

Reena is correct because _____

_____

_____ .

5 Complete the method for working out 35 × 16.

35 is equal to 5 × ☐

16 is equal to 2 × ☐

So, I can work out 35 × 16 by _____

_____

_____ .

6 **a)** Find the answer to this calculation:

6 × 2 × 3 × 5 × 4 × 5 = ☐

b) Explain why this is the same as 12 × 15 × 20.

_____

_____

_____

Reflect

Show why 3 × 4 × 6 is the same as 4 × 3 × 6.

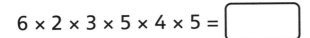

Date: _____

End of unit check

My journal

1 Show a partner how to work out one or more of the following:

45 × 7   132 × 6   78 ÷ 6   94 ÷ 5

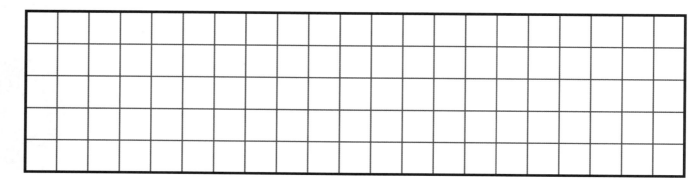

2 What is the same? What is different?

		H	T	O
		1	2	6
×				3
			1	8
			6	0
		3	0	0
		3	7	8

		H	T	O
		1	2	6
×				3
		3	7	8
			1	

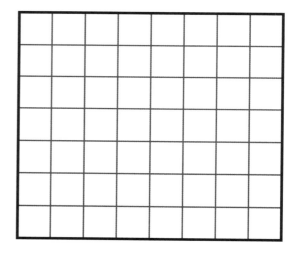

Power check

How do you feel about your work in this unit?   ?

Power puzzle

Lee is working out the remainder when 48 is divided by different numbers.

Number divided by	2	3	4	5	6	7	8
Remainder	0	0	0	3	0	6	0

Make sure you understand where each of the numbers comes from.

1 What would the table look like if Lee used 49 instead of 48?

Number divided by	2	3	4	5	6	7	8
Remainder							

2 What would the table look like if Lee now used 50?

Number divided by	2	3	4	5	6	7	8
Remainder							

3 What would the table look like if Lee used 51?

Number divided by	2	3	4	5	6	7	8
Remainder							

4 Explain any patterns that you notice.

_____

_____

_____

5 Here is another table. Work out what number Lee started with.

Number divided by	2	3	4	5	6	7	8
Remainder	1	0	3	2	3	6	3

Is there more than one answer?

Create your own table. Can a partner guess what number you started with?

Number divided by	2	3	4	5	6	7	8
Remainder							

Measure in km and m

1 Complete the bar models to help you convert each distance.

Barwich	3 km
Littleton	6 km
Newville	9,000 m

a) How far away is Barwich in metres?

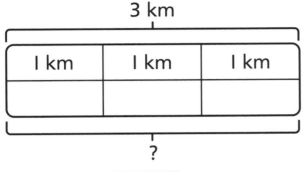

3 km = ☐ m

Barwich is ☐ metres away.

b) How far away is Littleton in metres?

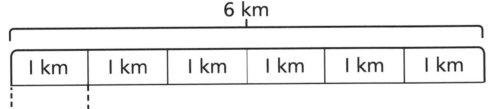

6 km = ☐ m

Littleton is ☐ metres away.

c) How far away is Newville in kilometres?

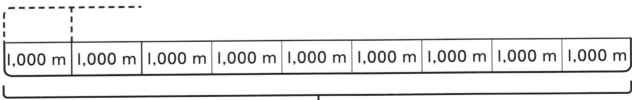

☐ km = 9,000 m

Newville is ☐ kilometres away.

2 Use these number lines to work out the equivalent distances.

| 0 km | 1 km | 2 km | 3 km | 4 km | 5 km |

| 0 m | 1,000 m | 2,000 m | 3,000 m | 4,000 m | 5,000 m |

a) 5 km = ▢ m

b) 1,500 m = ▢ $\frac{▢}{▢}$ km

c) ▢ m = $3\frac{1}{2}$ km

d) ▢ $\frac{▢}{▢}$ km = 1,250 m

3 Complete the equivalent distances.

a) 6 km = ▢ m

b) $4\frac{1}{2}$ km = ▢ m

c) ▢ km = 8,000 m

d) ▢ km = 7,500 m

e) 3,700 m = ▢ km and ▢ m

f) 4 km and 200 m = ▢ m

g) 7 km and 375 m = ▢ m

h) 6,050 m = ▢ km and ▢ m

4 The town council is planting flowers beside $9\frac{1}{2}$ km of roads.

What is the length of road in metres? ▢ m

5 The distance between any two stations is 1,000 m. Draw a route from A to B on the map.

Write down the number of kilometres the train travels on the route. ☐ km

A ○——○——○
○ = station
B

6 Write these distances in metres.

I can use what I know about kilometres to work out fractions of kilometres in metres.

CHALLENGE

a) $\frac{1}{2}$ km = ☐ m   d) $\frac{1}{4}$ km = ☐ m

b) $\frac{3}{4}$ km = ☐ m   e) $\frac{1}{5}$ km = ☐ m

c) $\frac{2}{5}$ km = ☐ m   f) $\frac{1}{10}$ km = ☐ m

Reflect

2,000 m + 500 m + 1 km = ☐ km

Use what you have learnt to explain how you would work out the answer.

_____
_____
_____

Date: _____

Perimeter on a grid

1 Liam draws a rectangle. He uses cubes to measure the length of each side. Each cube is 1 cm long.

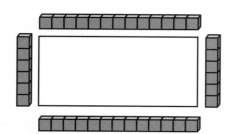

What is the perimeter of the rectangle?

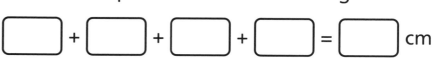

$\boxed{} + \boxed{} + \boxed{} + \boxed{} = \boxed{}$ cm

2 Find the perimeters of these rectangles.

a)

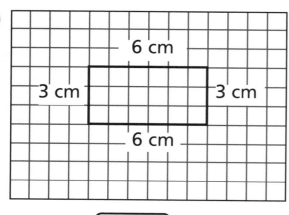

$\boxed{}$ cm

c)

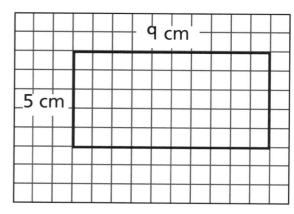

$\boxed{}$ cm

b)

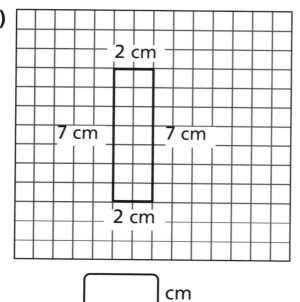

$\boxed{}$ cm

d)

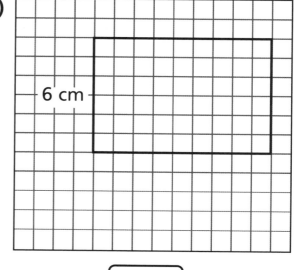

$\boxed{}$ cm

60

3 Annie says the perimeter of the rectangle is 11 cm.

Is Annie correct?

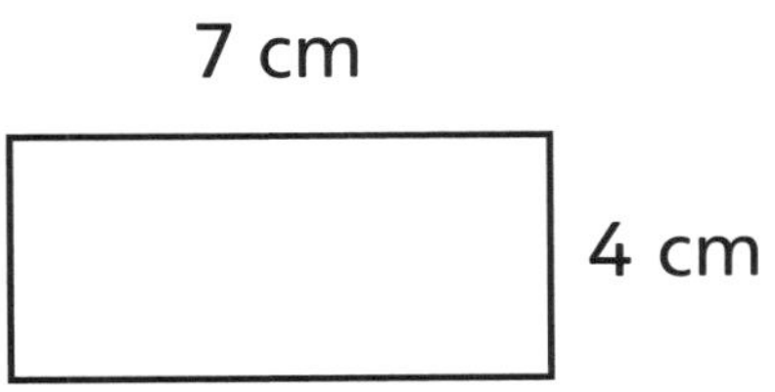

7 cm

4 cm

4 Each square has a length of 5 m.

a) Label the length and the width of this swimming pool.

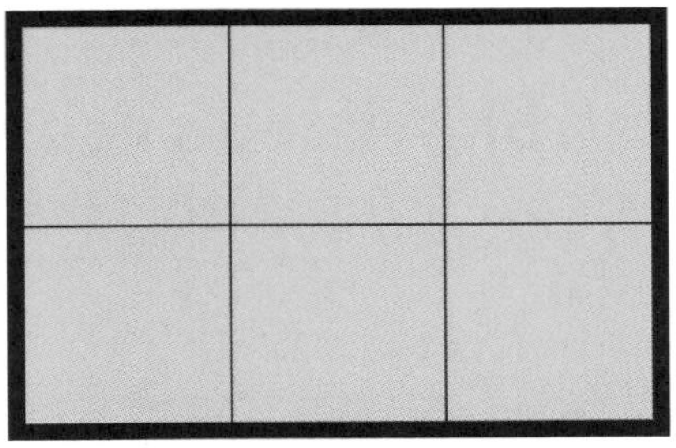

☐ m

☐ m

b) What is its perimeter? ☐ m

5 The school field is 50 m long and 23 m wide.

Jack runs the length of the field 3 times.

Evie runs around the perimeter once (1 time).

Who has run further?

6 A carpet company sells square rugs. Two sizes are shown.

CHALLENGE

5 m ☐   6 m ☐

a) Complete the table.

Side length	5 m	6 m	7 m	☐ m	☐ m
Perimeter	☐ m	☐ m	☐ m	32 m	40 m

b) What do you notice about the perimeters of the rugs? Why is this?

_____

_____

_____

Reflect

A classroom is a rectangle. Its length is 6 m. Its width is 5 m.

To work out the perimeter of this classroom, I would _____

_____

_____

Date: _____

Perimeter of a rectangle

1 Find the perimeter of the rectangles.

a)

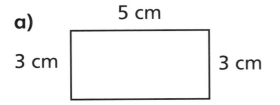

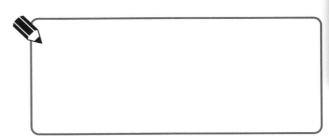

b)

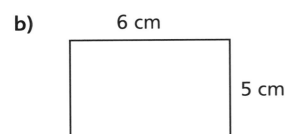

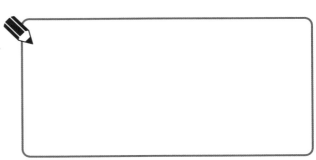

c)

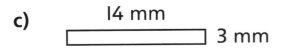

2 Find the missing lengths.

a) Perimeter = 14 cm

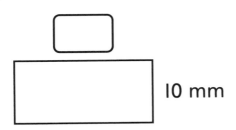

b) Perimeter = 100 mm

3 Draw lines to match each rectangle to its missing measurement.

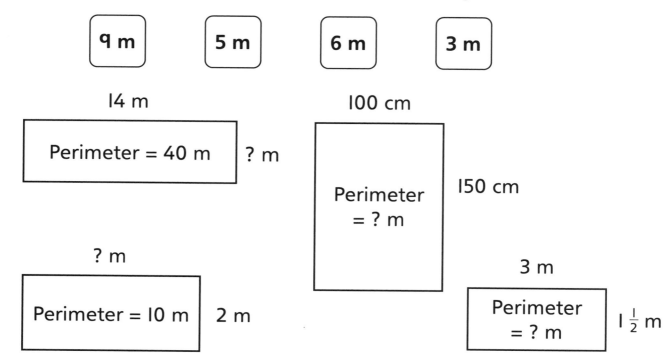

9 m   5 m   6 m   3 m

14 m

Perimeter = 40 m | ? m

100 cm

Perimeter = ? m | 150 cm

? m

Perimeter = 10 m | 2 m

3 m

Perimeter = ? m | $1\frac{1}{2}$ m

4 The perimeter of a rectangle is 16 cm.

a) Complete the table to show the different rectangles it could be.

Width	Length
1 cm	7 cm
2 cm	☐ cm
3 cm	☐ cm
4 cm	☐ cm

I think I can see a pattern between the length, the width and the perimeter.

b) What do you notice about the last shape in the table?

_____

5 This square table has side lengths of 70 cm.

CHALLENGE

a) What is its perimeter? ☐ cm

70 cm

b) Two tables are put next to each other.

What is the perimeter now? ☐ cm

Draw a diagram to show your answer.

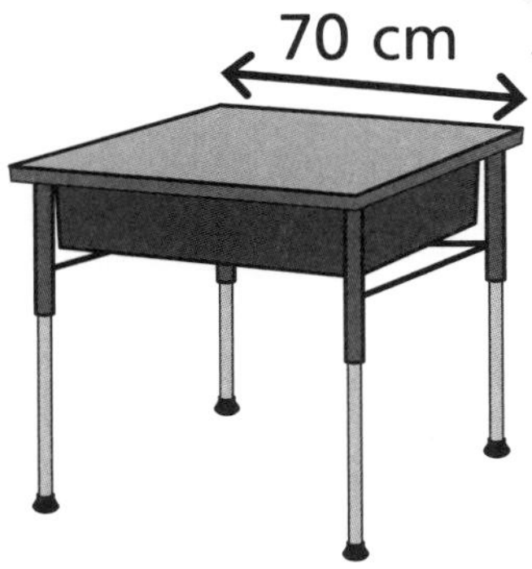

Reflect

The perimeter of a rectangle is 12 cm. Its width is 1 cm.

Explain what to do to find out its length.

Date: _____

Perimeter of rectilinear shapes

1 A gardener uses wooden edging around a flower bed.

Each piece of edging is I m long.

⊢————⊣ = I metre of edging

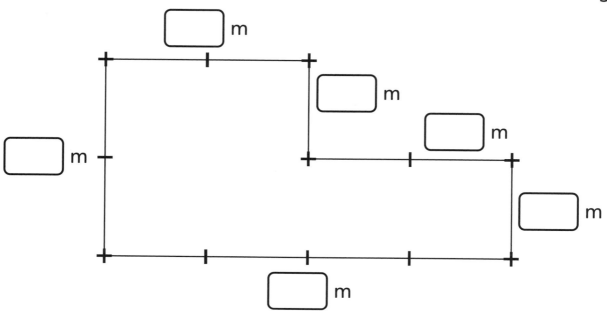

a) Complete the measurements of each side.

b) Work out the perimeter of the flower bed.

The perimeter of the flower bed is [ ] m.

2 Find the perimeter of this shape.

[ ] cm

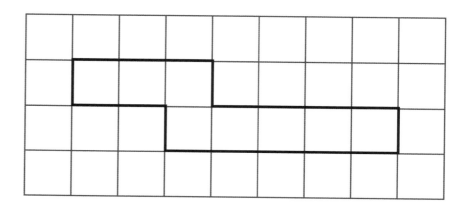

3 What is the perimeter of each shape?

a)

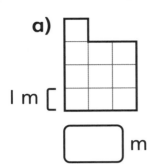

I m [

[　　　] m

c)

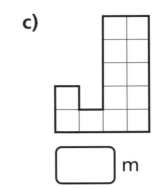

[　　　] m

b)

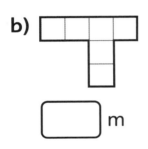

[　　　] m

d)

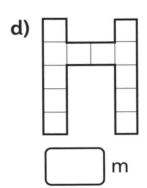

[　　　] m

4 Lottie is designing a badge in the shape of the letter L.

The lengths of its sides are: 7 cm, 2 cm, 4 cm, 3 cm, 3 cm and 5 cm.

I cm [

a) The perimeter of the badge is

[　　　] cm.

b) Use the measurements to draw the badge. The first two lines have been done for you.

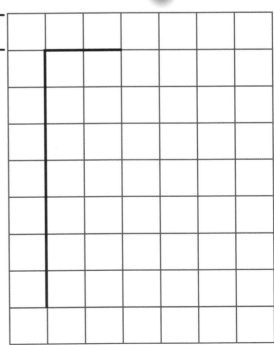

5 **a)** Use the squared paper below to draw a rectilinear outline of a factory with two chimneys.

CHALLENGE

Keep to the squares. Your factory needs to have a flat roof.

b) Label the length of each side.

c) What is the perimeter of the factory? _____

Reflect

Amy is working out the perimeter of this shape.

She says that it is 26 cm.

Is Amy correct? Yes / No (Circle your choice.)

Discuss why with a partner.

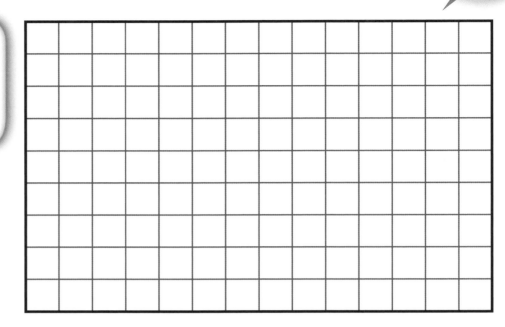

I cm

1	2	3	4	5			
26				6			
25				7			
24				8			
23				9	10	11	12
22							13
21	20	19	18	17	16	15	14

Find missing lengths in rectilinear shapes

1 A zookeeper is putting logs into a shape to make sure the otters do not escape!

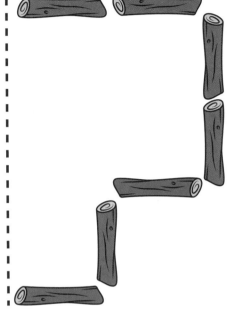

a) She has nearly finished.

How many more logs does she need to finish the shape?

b) What is the perimeter of the shape?

[   ] logs.

2 a) What is the length of A? [   ] cm

b) What is the length of B? [   ] cm

c) Discuss with a partner how you can work them out without counting squares.

7 cm

6 cm

A

2 cm

2 cm

B

3 Find the measurement of each missing side, then calculate the perimeters of the two shapes.

a)

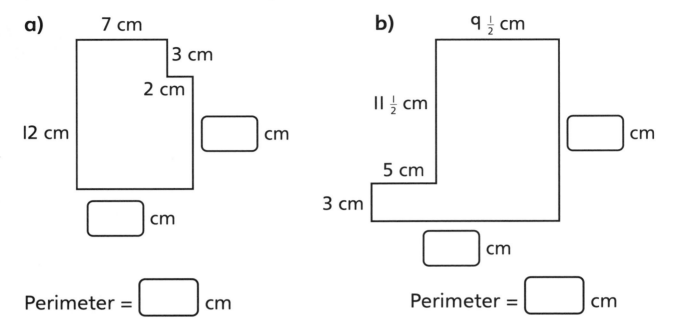

7 cm
3 cm
2 cm
12 cm
☐ cm
☐ cm

Perimeter = ☐ cm

b)

$9\frac{1}{2}$ cm
$11\frac{1}{2}$ cm
5 cm
3 cm
☐ cm
☐ cm

Perimeter = ☐ cm

4 This rectilinear shape does not have all its measurements marked.

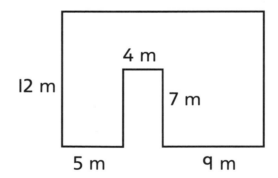

4 m
12 m
7 m
5 m
9 m

Work out the perimeter.

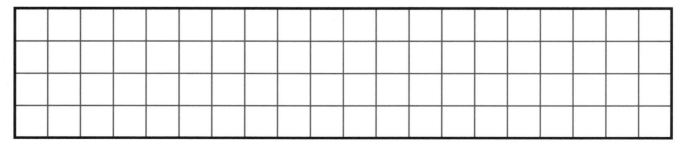

The perimeter is ☐ m.

5 The junctions in this town are 20 m apart.

A taxi drives 160 m and ends up where it began. It makes a rectilinear shape.

Use two colours to show two different routes the taxi could take.

Are there more than two routes? Can you find a rule?

CHALLENGE

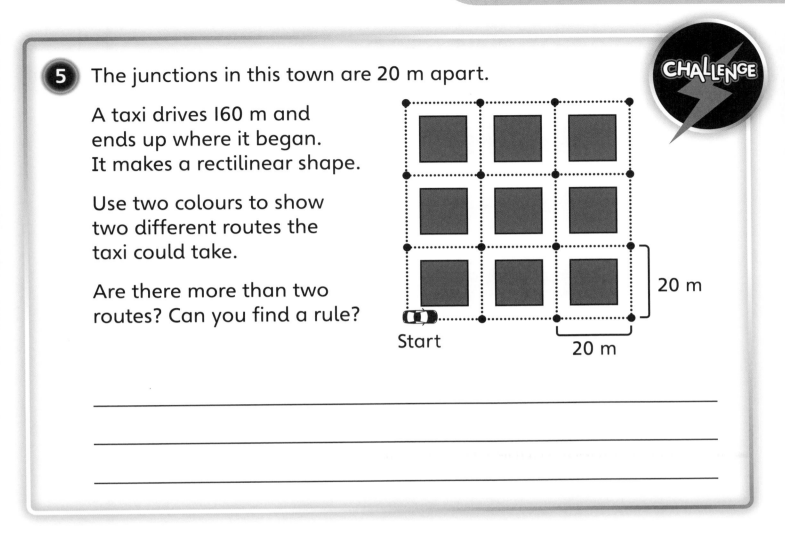

Start

20 m

20 m

_____

_____

_____

Reflect

Design a rectilinear perimeter problem for a partner to answer.

Explain how you expect your partner to work out the perimeter.

_____

_____

_____

_____

Date: _____

Perimeter of polygons

1 Calculate the perimeter of each regular polygon.

a)

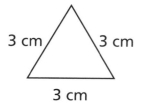

Perimeter = ☐ cm

d)

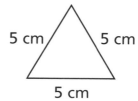

Perimeter = ☐ cm

b)

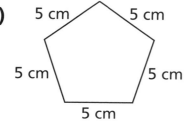

Perimeter = ☐ cm

e)

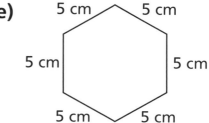

Perimeter = ☐ cm

c)

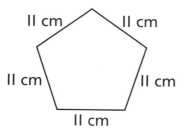

Perimeter = ☐ cm

f)

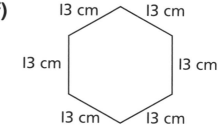

Perimeter = ☐ cm

72

2 Calculate the perimeter of each polygon.

a)

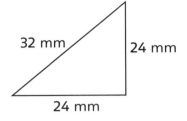

Perimeter = ☐ mm

c)

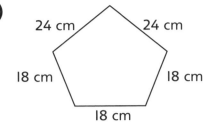

Perimeter = ☐ cm

b)

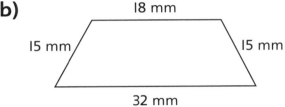

Perimeter = ☐ mm

3 Calculate the missing side lengths of these polygons.

a)

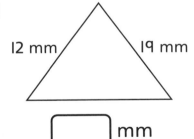

☐ mm

Perimeter = 50 mm

b)

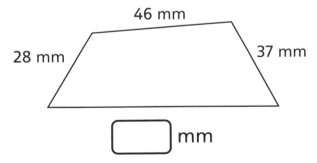

☐ mm

Perimeter = 160 mm

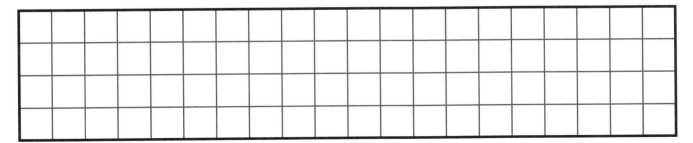

73

4 Calculate the missing side lengths of these regular polygons.

a)

Perimeter = 85 cm

b)

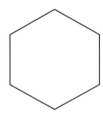

Perimeter = 126 cm

c)

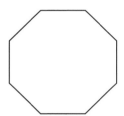

Perimeter = 448 cm

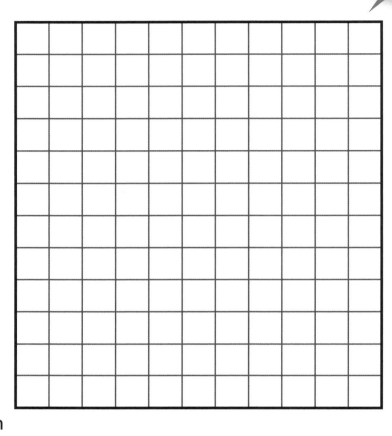

Reflect

Draw and label a diagram to show a regular polygon with a perimeter of 48 cm. Compare your diagrams as a class.

Date: _____

End of unit check

My journal

→ Textbook 4B p100

The distance between two dots on the same line is I rod.

Draw three different shapes, each with a perimeter of 12 rods.

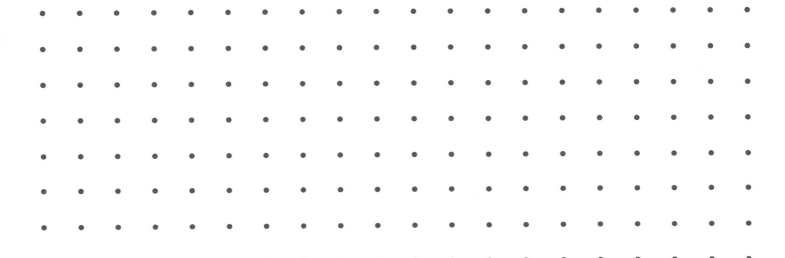

Explain how you decided what the side lengths of your shapes should be.

_____

_____

Power check

How do you feel about your work in this unit?

Power puzzle

Aaron has dropped 2 chocolate bars on the floor.

They have broken into 8 pieces.

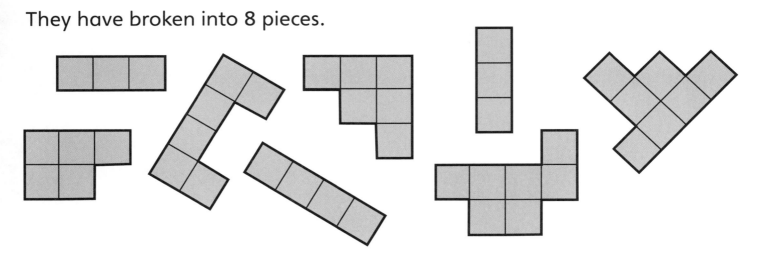

Use squared paper to copy and cut out each of these 8 shapes.

a) The 2 chocolate bars were both rectangles, but they had different areas. Put the pieces back together to make both rectangles. You can turn the pieces over if you need to.

b) What is the perimeter of each shape?

Make your own puzzle by cutting up two rectangles. Give a partner a clue about the rectangles. Can they find their areas?

Date: _____

Count beyond 1

1 What mixed numbers are shown here?

a)

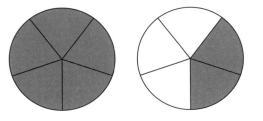

b)

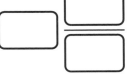

c)

  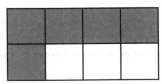

2 What mixed numbers are shown here?

a)

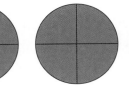

b)

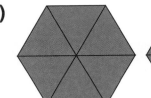 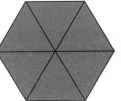 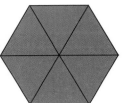

3 Shade in

a) $2\frac{1}{4}$

b) $3\frac{4}{5}$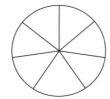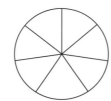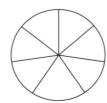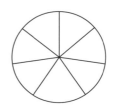

c) $3\frac{4}{7}$

4 Max says it's not possible to write this as a mixed number.

You can't see what the first two circles are split into, so you can't write it as a mixed number.

Max

Explain why Max is incorrect.

_____

_____

5 Represent $2 \frac{3}{4}$.

6 Here is a mixed number.

CHALLENGE

What mixed number is shown?

Write your answer in a different way.

Reflect

There are two parts to a mixed number.
Explain what they are.

Date: _____

Partition a mixed number

1 Complete the part-whole models.

a)

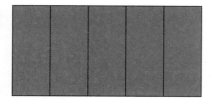 

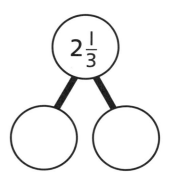

b)

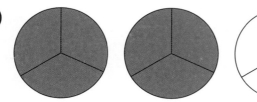

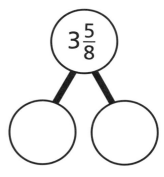

c)

 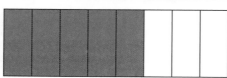

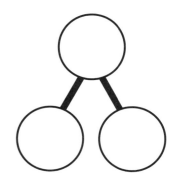

d)

 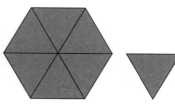

2 Complete the part-whole models.

a)

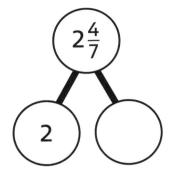

d)

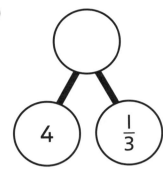

b)

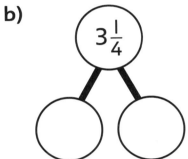

e)

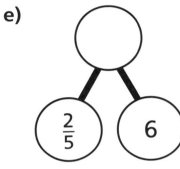

c)

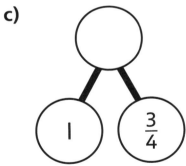

f)

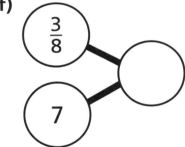

3 Complete the calculations.

a) $2 + \frac{1}{5} =$ ⬜ ⬜/⬜

c) $4 + \frac{2}{3} =$ ⬜ ⬜/⬜

b) $3 + \frac{1}{4} =$ ⬜ ⬜/⬜

d) $5 + \frac{7}{10} =$ ⬜ ⬜/⬜

4 Isla has made 4 and $\frac{3}{4}$ circles using quarter circles.

How many different ways could she complete a part-whole model to show the same total?

CHALLENGE

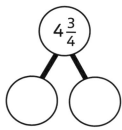 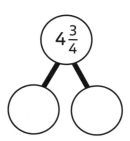 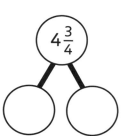

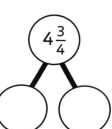 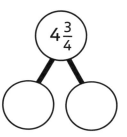 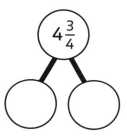

Reflect

Write down your own mixed number.
Ask a partner to partition the number.

Date: _____

Number lines with mixed numbers

1 Complete the number lines.

a)

0   $\frac{1}{3}$ $\frac{2}{3}$ 2

b)
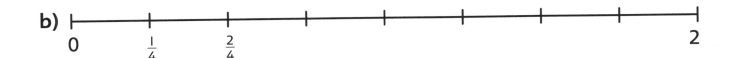

0   $\frac{1}{4}$ $\frac{2}{4}$ 2

c)
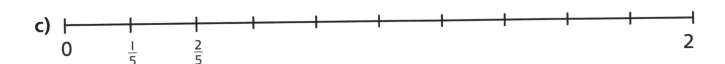

0   $\frac{1}{5}$ $\frac{2}{5}$ 2

2 Max is counting up in $\frac{1}{3}$s from 5 to 7. Help him complete his count.

5        $5\frac{1}{3}$

Max

3 What numbers are the arrows pointing to?

a)

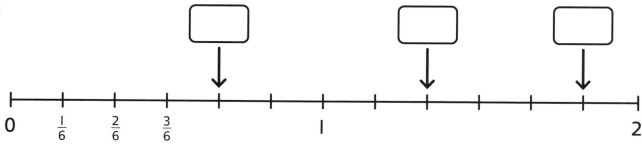

b)

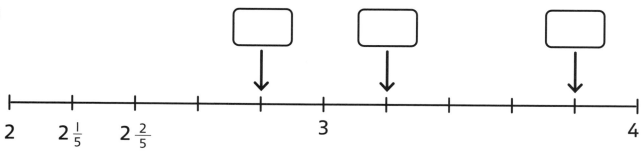

c)

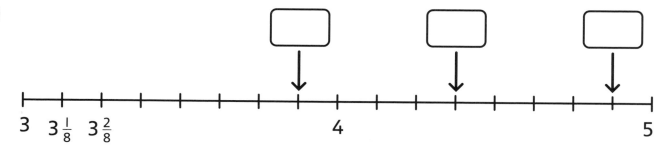

4 Emma says the arrow is pointing to $2\frac{3}{4}$.

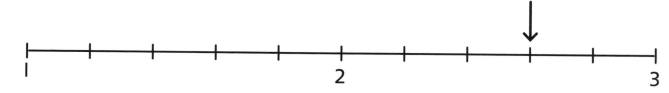

Is Emma correct? Explain your answer.

_____

_____

5 What fraction is the arrow pointing to on each number line?

a)

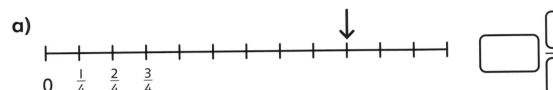

b)

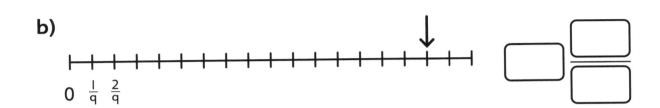

6 Draw an arrow from each fraction to its place on the number lines.

a) I whole and $\frac{1}{3}$ $3\frac{1}{3}$ $2\frac{1}{2}$

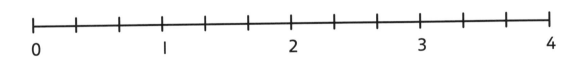

b) $1\frac{4}{6}$ 2 wholes and $\frac{5}{6}$ $2\frac{1}{3}$

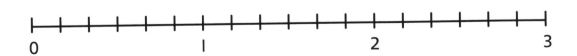

Reflect

Count in $\frac{1}{3}$s from 5 to 8 as a class. Did you get it correct first time?

Date: _____

Compare and order mixed numbers

1 Circle the fraction that is the greatest.

a)

$1\frac{4}{5}$

$3\frac{1}{5}$

b)

$1\frac{5}{8}$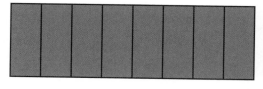

$1\frac{3}{8}$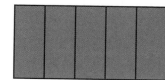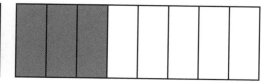

2 Circle the fraction that is the least.

a)

$2\frac{3}{4}$

$2\frac{1}{4}$

b)

$3\frac{4}{5}$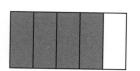

$2\frac{1}{5}$

3 Complete the sentences using the phrases 'greater than' or 'less than'.

a) $2\frac{1}{3}$ is _____ $1\frac{2}{3}$.

b) $1\frac{7}{8}$ is _____ $1\frac{2}{8}$.

c) $5\frac{1}{3}$ is _____ $5\frac{2}{3}$.

d) $5\frac{1}{9}$ is _____ $3\frac{8}{9}$.

4 Use < or > to compare the mixed numbers.

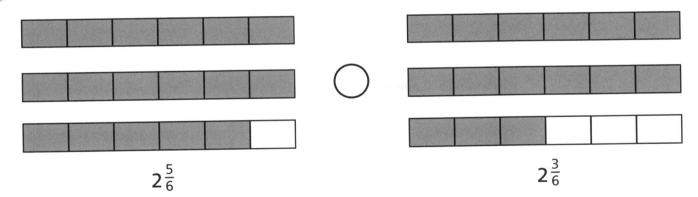

$2\frac{5}{6}$ $2\frac{3}{6}$

5 Complete the number sentences using < or >.

a) $4\frac{2}{3}$ ◯ $3\frac{1}{3}$

b) $2\frac{7}{10}$ ◯ $5\frac{7}{10}$

c) $3\frac{3}{5}$ ◯ $3\frac{4}{5}$

d) $2\frac{1}{5}$ ◯ 2

6 Put the following mixed numbers in order. Start with the greatest number.

$4\frac{5}{6}$ $3\frac{1}{6}$ $4\frac{3}{6}$

7 Draw lines from each fraction to show where it belongs on the number line.

CHALLENGE

$2\frac{1}{3}$ $3\frac{1}{3}$ $1\frac{2}{3}$ $\frac{2}{3}$

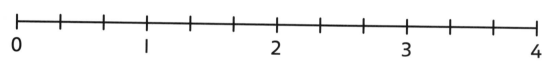

0   1   2   3   4

Use your answer to help you put the mixed numbers in order. Start with the smallest number.

_____

Reflect

Explain how you would compare two mixed numbers.

_____

_____

Convert mixed numbers to improper fractions

→ Textbook 4B p120

 a) Count how many thirds.

$$\frac{\boxed{}}{3}$$

b) Count how many quarters.

 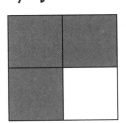

$$\frac{\boxed{}}{4}$$

c) Count how many sixths.

 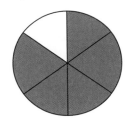

$$\frac{\boxed{}}{6}$$

2 Emma thinks that $2\frac{1}{5}$ is the same as $\frac{11}{5}$.

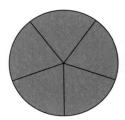  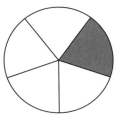

Explain why Emma is correct.

_____

_____

3 Write each mixed number as an improper fraction.

a) $4\frac{1}{3} = \dfrac{\boxed{}}{3}$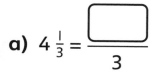

b) $2\frac{2}{7} = \dfrac{\boxed{}}{7}$

4 Shade the fractions and then write each as an improper fraction.

a) $3\frac{1}{5} = \dfrac{\boxed{}}{5}$

b) $3\frac{1}{4}$

c) $1\frac{7}{10}$

5 Complete the number lines using improper fractions and mixed numbers.

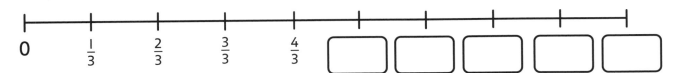

$0 \qquad \frac{1}{3} \qquad \frac{2}{3} \qquad \frac{3}{3} \qquad \frac{4}{3}$ ☐ ☐ ☐ ☐ ☐

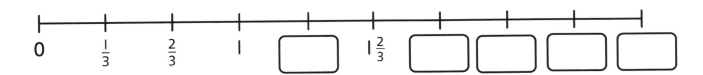

$0 \qquad \frac{1}{3} \qquad \frac{2}{3} \qquad 1 \qquad$ ☐ $\qquad 1\frac{2}{3}$ ☐ ☐ ☐ ☐

CHALLENGE

6 **a)** How many $\frac{1}{2}$s in $5\frac{1}{2}$? Draw a diagram to help you.

There are ☐ $\frac{1}{2}$s in $5\frac{1}{2}$.

I will use my answer and drawing to part **a)**.

b) How many $\frac{1}{4}$s in $5\frac{1}{2}$?

There are ☐ $\frac{1}{4}$s in $5\frac{1}{2}$.

Reflect

Explain to a partner how you can use a diagram to show that $1\frac{2}{3}$ is the same as $\frac{5}{3}$.

Date: _____

Convert improper fractions to mixed numbers

1 **a)** Shade in $\frac{8}{3}$.

b) Write $\frac{8}{3}$ as a mixed number.

2 **a)** Shade in $\frac{13}{8}$.

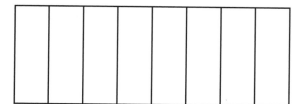 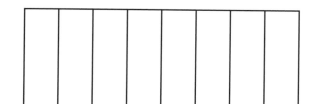

b) Write $\frac{13}{8}$ as a mixed number.

3 **a)** Shade in $\frac{13}{4}$.

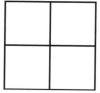 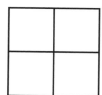  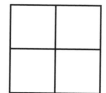

b) Write $\frac{13}{4}$ as a mixed number.

4 Use the diagrams to write each number as a mixed number.

a) $\dfrac{17}{5}$ = ⬭ $\dfrac{□}{□}$

b) $\dfrac{13}{10}$ = ⬭ $\dfrac{□}{□}$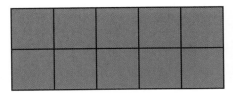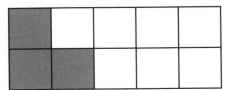

c) $\dfrac{13}{6}$

5 Kate has these cubes. She packs them into boxes.
Each box holds 6 cubes.

How many boxes does she need?

Write your answer as a mixed number.

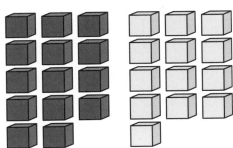

⬭ $\dfrac{□}{□}$

6 **a)** Max has $\frac{19}{5}$ litres of juice.

Show Max's juice on the diagrams

b) Emma has $4\frac{1}{5}$ litres of juice.

Show Emma's juice on the diagrams

c) Who has more juice? _____

Reflect

Explain how you can use a diagram to help you write $\frac{13}{3}$ as a mixed number.

_____

_____

_____

Equivalent fractions

1 Shade an equivalent fraction to the fraction given.

Write down the equivalent fractions.

a)

| $\frac{1}{3}$ | $\frac{1}{3}$ | $\frac{1}{3}$ |

| $\frac{1}{6}$ | $\frac{1}{6}$ | $\frac{1}{6}$ | $\frac{1}{6}$ | $\frac{1}{6}$ | $\frac{1}{6}$ |

$\frac{2}{3} = \frac{\boxed{}}{6}$

b)

| $\frac{1}{8}$ | $\frac{1}{8}$ | $\frac{1}{8}$ | $\frac{1}{8}$ | $\frac{1}{8}$ | $\frac{1}{8}$ | $\frac{1}{8}$ | $\frac{1}{8}$ |

| $\frac{1}{4}$ | | | |

$\frac{\boxed{}}{\boxed{}} = \frac{\boxed{}}{\boxed{}}$

c)

| $\frac{1}{10}$ | | | | | | | | | |

| $\frac{1}{8}$ | | | | | | | | |

$\frac{\boxed{}}{\boxed{}} = \frac{\boxed{}}{\boxed{}} = \frac{\boxed{}}{\boxed{}}$

95

2 Use the fraction wall to say whether these fractions are equivalent or not.

a) $\frac{5}{8}$ _____ equal to $\frac{1}{2}$.

b) $\frac{3}{6}$ _____ equal to $\frac{3}{9}$.

c) $\frac{4}{8}$ _____ equal to $\frac{1}{4}$.

d) $\frac{4}{6}$ _____ equal to $\frac{6}{9}$.

e) $\frac{4}{4}$ _____ equal to $\frac{9}{9}$.

$\frac{1}{3}$		$\frac{1}{3}$		$\frac{1}{3}$	

$\frac{1}{4}$ $\frac{1}{4}$ $\frac{1}{4}$ $\frac{1}{4}$

$\frac{1}{6}$ $\frac{1}{6}$ $\frac{1}{6}$ $\frac{1}{6}$ $\frac{1}{6}$ $\frac{1}{6}$

$\frac{1}{8}$ $\frac{1}{8}$ $\frac{1}{8}$ $\frac{1}{8}$ $\frac{1}{8}$ $\frac{1}{8}$ $\frac{1}{8}$ $\frac{1}{8}$

$\frac{1}{9}$ $\frac{1}{9}$ $\frac{1}{9}$ $\frac{1}{9}$ $\frac{1}{9}$ $\frac{1}{9}$ $\frac{1}{9}$ $\frac{1}{9}$ $\frac{1}{9}$

3 Use the fraction strips to show that these statements are true.

a) $\frac{1}{3}$ is equal to $\frac{3}{9}$.

b) $\frac{2}{5}$ is equal to $\frac{4}{10}$.

c) $\frac{1}{4}$ is equal to $\frac{2}{8}$ which is equal to $\frac{3}{12}$.

4 Lee says that he has shown the same fraction as Zac because they have both shaded in 3 sections of their strips.

CHALLENGE

Lee   Zac

Do you agree? Explain how you know.

_____

_____

_____

Reflect

Explain how a fraction wall shows equivalent fractions.

1			
$\frac{1}{2}$		$\frac{1}{2}$	
$\frac{1}{3}$	$\frac{1}{3}$		$\frac{1}{3}$
$\frac{1}{4}$	$\frac{1}{4}$	$\frac{1}{4}$	$\frac{1}{4}$

_____

_____

_____

Date: _____

↑ Textbook 4B p132

Equivalent fraction families

1 Use the shapes to find equivalent fractions.

a)

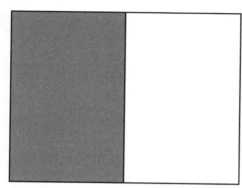 

$\dfrac{1}{2} = \dfrac{\boxed{}}{6}$

b)

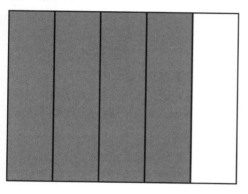 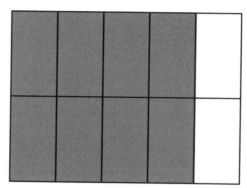

$\dfrac{4}{5} = \dfrac{\boxed{}}{10}$

c)

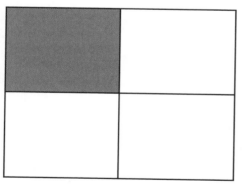 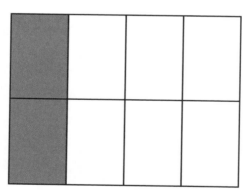

$\dfrac{1}{4} = \dfrac{\boxed{}}{\boxed{}}$

d)

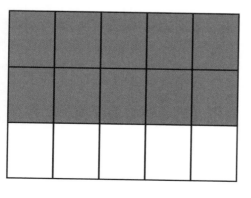

$\dfrac{10}{15} = \dfrac{\boxed{}}{\boxed{}}$

2 Find the missing numbers.

a) $\dfrac{1}{2} = \dfrac{\boxed{}}{8}$

b) $\dfrac{3}{4} = \dfrac{15}{\boxed{}}$

c) $\dfrac{3}{5} = \dfrac{9}{\boxed{}}$

d) $\dfrac{1}{6} = \dfrac{\boxed{}}{24}$

e) $\dfrac{\boxed{}}{7} = \dfrac{6}{21}$

f) $\dfrac{20}{24} = \dfrac{\boxed{}}{\boxed{}} = \dfrac{\boxed{}}{\boxed{}}$

3 Draw lines to connect the equivalent fractions.

$\dfrac{1}{5}$ $\dfrac{2}{3}$ $\dfrac{10}{20}$ $\dfrac{5}{6}$ $\dfrac{2}{9}$ $\dfrac{11}{12}$

$\dfrac{4}{6}$ $\dfrac{6}{27}$ $\dfrac{55}{60}$ $\dfrac{4}{20}$ $\dfrac{1}{2}$ $\dfrac{10}{12}$

4 Find numbers that can make the fractions equivalent.

a)
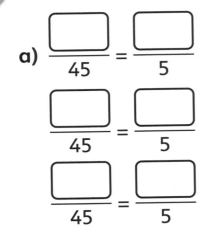

b)
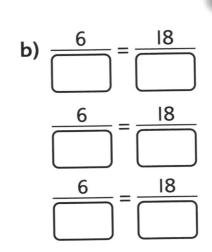

5 Write three equivalent fractions for each fraction.

a) $\frac{5}{6}$

b) $\frac{10}{10}$

c) $\frac{1}{8}$

6 Prove that these fractions are equivalent. Explain your reasoning to a partner.

$\frac{12}{20}$ $\frac{9}{15}$

CHALLENGE

Reflect

Explain how to find fractions that are equivalent to $\frac{1}{4}$.

Simplify fractions

1 What fraction of each shape is shaded?

Simplify your fraction.

a)

$$\frac{2}{10} = \frac{1}{\boxed{}}$$

÷ 2 (top)
÷ 2 (bottom)

b)

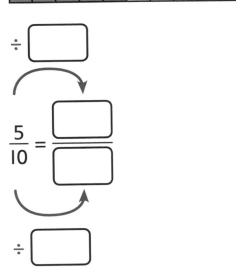

$$\frac{5}{10} = \frac{\boxed{}}{\boxed{}}$$

2 What fraction of each shape is shaded?

Give your answer in its simplest form.

a)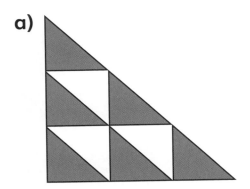

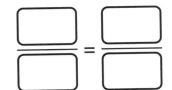

b)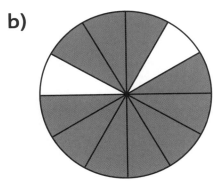

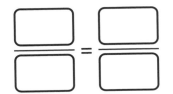

3 Draw lines to match each diagram to its fraction in its simplest form.

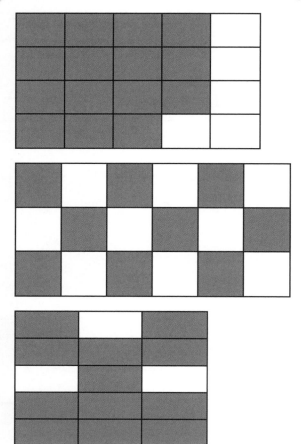

$\dfrac{2}{5}$

$\dfrac{4}{5}$

$\dfrac{1}{3}$

$\dfrac{1}{2}$

$\dfrac{3}{4}$

4 A group of friends are all given the same chocolate bar. After a week they have eaten different amounts.

I ate $\dfrac{3}{5}$ of my chocolate.

Zac

Richard

I ate $\dfrac{8}{20}$ of my chocolate.

I ate $\dfrac{8}{10}$ of my chocolate.

Ambika

Who ate the least amount of chocolate?

_____ ate the least amount of chocolate.

5 What is the most efficient way to simplify these fractions?

a) $\frac{12}{30}$ _____

_____

b) $\frac{8}{32}$ _____

_____

c) $\frac{18}{36}$ _____

_____

6 Lee thinks that this fraction cannot be simplified any further.

Do you agree? Explain your answer.

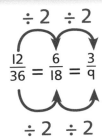

_____

_____

Reflect

How do you know when a fraction is in its simplest form?

_____

_____

Date: _____

End of unit check

My journal

How many fractions can you make that are equivalent to the fractions below?

$$\frac{3}{12} \qquad \frac{6}{18} \qquad \frac{11}{20}$$

What is the simplest fraction you can make for each one?

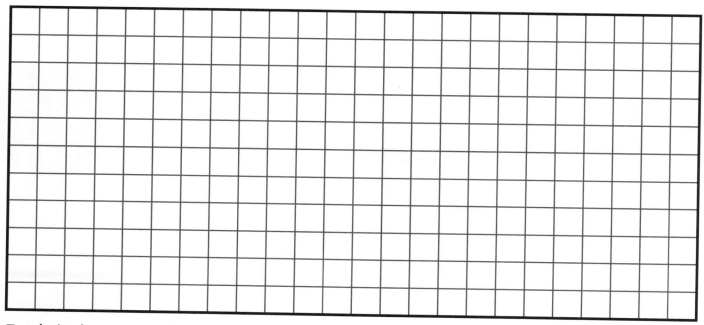

Explain how you know you have found the simplest fractions.

_____

_____

Power check

How do you feel about your work in this unit?

Power play

Play this game with a partner.

Take it in turns to roll a dice, move your counter and answer the questions. If you cannot answer a question, go back to the start.

Go forward 2 spaces →	Draw a fraction less than $\frac{1}{2}$	Can $\frac{11}{13}$ be simplified? Explain …		**Finish**
Write a fraction equivalent to $\frac{15}{20}$		Draw a fraction equivalent to $\frac{1}{3}$		Write a fraction equivalent to $\frac{1}{9}$
Go back to the start ↓		Go to the smiley face		☺
Draw a fraction equivalent to $\frac{3}{4}$		Draw a fraction less than $\frac{1}{3}$		Draw a fraction equivalent to $\frac{22}{33}$
Start		↑ Go back 3 spaces	Can $\frac{21}{24}$ be simplified? Explain …	Miss a go

Draw a board like this to create your own game.

Date: _____

↑ Textbook 4B p144

Add and subtract two or more fractions

1 Work out

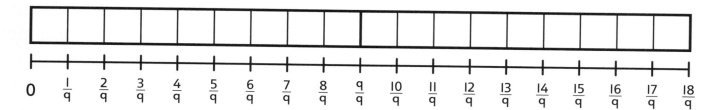

a) $\dfrac{4}{9} + \dfrac{4}{9} = \dfrac{\boxed{}}{\boxed{}}$

d) $\dfrac{8}{9} - \dfrac{3}{9} = \dfrac{\boxed{}}{\boxed{}}$

b) $\dfrac{5}{9} + \dfrac{6}{9} = \dfrac{\boxed{}}{\boxed{}}$

e) $\dfrac{11}{9} - \dfrac{5}{9} = \dfrac{\boxed{}}{\boxed{}}$

c) $\dfrac{7}{9} + \dfrac{8}{9} = \dfrac{\boxed{}}{\boxed{}}$

f) $\dfrac{15}{9} - \dfrac{11}{9} = \dfrac{\boxed{}}{\boxed{}}$

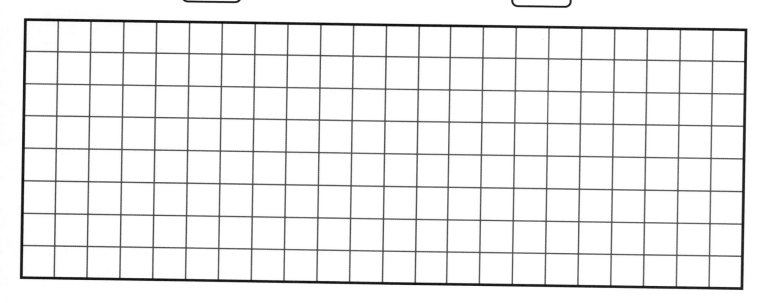

2 Work out the following calculations.

Give your answers as improper fractions.

I could draw a fraction strip to help me.

a) $\dfrac{3}{4} + \dfrac{3}{4} = \dfrac{\boxed{}}{\boxed{}}$

d) $\dfrac{3}{10} + \dfrac{1}{10} + \dfrac{9}{10} = \dfrac{\boxed{}}{\boxed{}}$

b) $\dfrac{2}{5} + \dfrac{4}{5} = \dfrac{\boxed{}}{\boxed{}}$

e) $\dfrac{3}{5} + \dfrac{3}{5} + \dfrac{3}{5} = \dfrac{\boxed{}}{\boxed{}}$

c) $\dfrac{11}{12} - \dfrac{5}{12} = \dfrac{\boxed{}}{\boxed{}}$

f) 8 ninths + 5 ninths $= \dfrac{\boxed{}}{\boxed{}}$

3 Match the calculation to the correct answer.

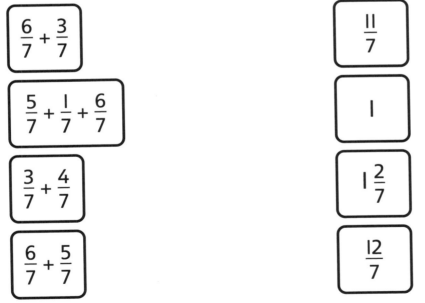

$\dfrac{6}{7} + \dfrac{3}{7}$

$\dfrac{5}{7} + \dfrac{1}{7} + \dfrac{6}{7}$

$\dfrac{3}{7} + \dfrac{4}{7}$

$\dfrac{6}{7} + \dfrac{5}{7}$

$\dfrac{11}{7}$

1

$1\dfrac{2}{7}$

$\dfrac{12}{7}$

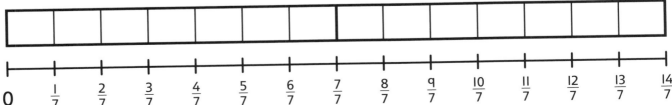

$0 \qquad \dfrac{1}{7} \qquad \dfrac{2}{7} \qquad \dfrac{3}{7} \qquad \dfrac{4}{7} \qquad \dfrac{5}{7} \qquad \dfrac{6}{7} \qquad \dfrac{7}{7} \qquad \dfrac{8}{7} \qquad \dfrac{9}{7} \qquad \dfrac{10}{7} \qquad \dfrac{11}{7} \qquad \dfrac{12}{7} \qquad \dfrac{13}{7} \qquad \dfrac{14}{7}$

4 Fred works out this calculation

$$\frac{3}{8} + \frac{7}{8} = \frac{10}{16}$$

a) What mistake has Fred made? _____

b) What is the correct answer? _____

5 Find the missing numbers.

CHALLENGE

a) $\frac{4}{5} + \frac{\boxed{}}{5} = \frac{7}{5}$ $\frac{4}{5} + \frac{\boxed{}}{5} = 1\frac{2}{5}$ $\frac{4}{5} + \frac{\boxed{}}{5} = 1\frac{3}{5}$

b) $\frac{11}{13} - \frac{\boxed{}}{13} = \frac{7}{13}$ $\frac{7}{8} - \frac{\boxed{}}{8} = \frac{3}{8}$ $\frac{\boxed{}}{6} + \frac{1}{6} = 1$

c) $\frac{15}{8} = \frac{3}{8} + \frac{\boxed{}}{8} + \frac{\boxed{}}{8}$ $\frac{15}{8} = \frac{4}{8} + \frac{\boxed{}}{8} + \frac{\boxed{}}{8}$

$\frac{15}{8} = \frac{5}{8} + \frac{\boxed{}}{8} + \frac{\boxed{}}{8}$ $\frac{15}{8} = \frac{6}{8} + \frac{\boxed{}}{8} + \frac{\boxed{}}{8}$

Reflect

Draw a diagram to show that $\frac{4}{5} + \frac{4}{5} = \frac{8}{5}$.

Add fractions and mixed numbers

→ Textbook 4B p148

1 Work out these calculations. Use the number lines to help you.

a) $1\frac{1}{4} + \frac{1}{4}$

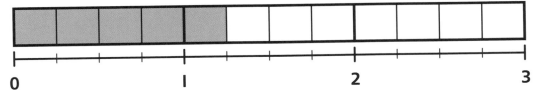

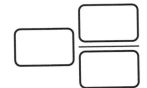

b) $1\frac{1}{4} + \frac{2}{4}$

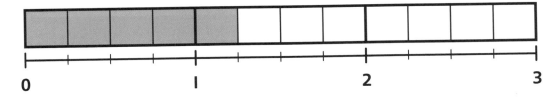

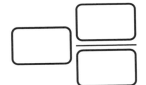

c) $1\frac{1}{4} + \frac{3}{4}$

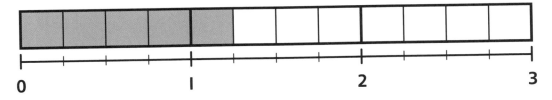

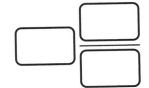

d) $1\frac{1}{4} + \frac{5}{4}$

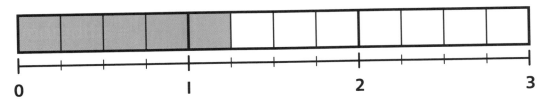

109

2 **a)** Work out $2\frac{2}{3} + \frac{2}{3}$.

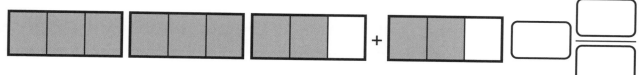

b) Work out $1\frac{4}{5} + \frac{3}{5}$.

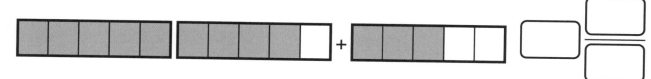

3 Work out these calculations. Use the fraction strip to help you.

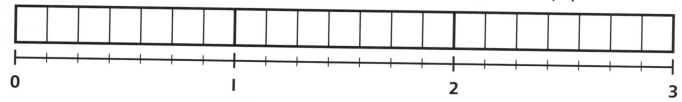

a) $1\frac{4}{7} + \frac{2}{7} = \boxed{}\, \frac{\boxed{}}{\boxed{}}$

c) $1\frac{4}{7} + \frac{5}{7} = \boxed{}\, \frac{\boxed{}}{\boxed{}}$

b) $1\frac{4}{7} + \frac{3}{7} = \boxed{}\, \frac{\boxed{}}{\boxed{}}$

d) $1\frac{4}{7} + \frac{6}{7} = \boxed{}\, \frac{\boxed{}}{\boxed{}}$

4 What is the total mass of the boxes?

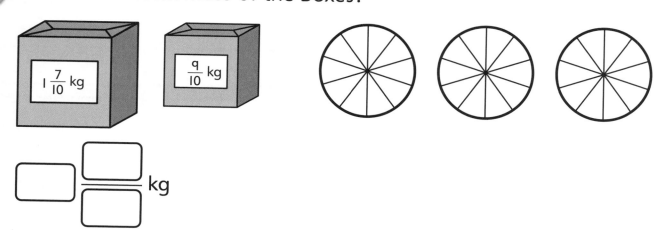

$\boxed{}\, \frac{\boxed{}}{\boxed{}}$ kg

5 Bella has $3\frac{3}{4}$ pizzas.

Aki has $\frac{3}{4}$ pizzas.

How many pizzas do they have in total?

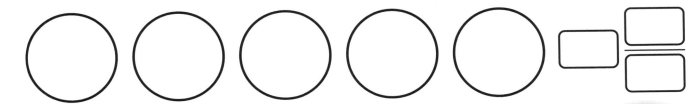

6 Work out the missing numbers.

CHALLENGE

a) $2\frac{4}{5} + \frac{\boxed{}}{5} = 3\frac{3}{5}$

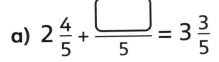

b) $1\frac{\boxed{}}{7} + \frac{6}{7} = 3\frac{3}{7}$

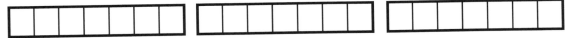

Reflect

Explain how you can add a mixed number to a fraction.

Date: _____

Subtract from mixed numbers

1 Work out the subtractions.

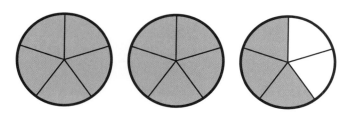

a) $2\frac{3}{5} - \frac{2}{5} = \boxed{}\dfrac{\boxed{}}{\boxed{}}$

c) $2\frac{3}{5} - \frac{4}{5} = \boxed{}\dfrac{\boxed{}}{\boxed{}}$

b) $2\frac{3}{5} - \frac{3}{5} = \boxed{}$

d) $2\frac{3}{5} - \frac{7}{5} = \boxed{}\dfrac{\boxed{}}{\boxed{}}$

2 Last week Rusty the dog ate $2\frac{7}{10}$ kg of dog food. This week he ate $\frac{9}{10}$ kg less than last week.

How much dog food did Rusty eat this week?

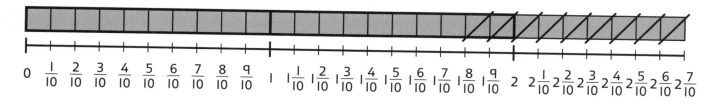

$2\frac{7}{10} - \dfrac{\boxed{}}{\boxed{}} = \boxed{}\dfrac{\boxed{}}{\boxed{}}$ kg

3 Complete each calculation.

a) $1\frac{7}{8} - \frac{3}{8} = \boxed{}\ \dfrac{\boxed{}}{\boxed{}}$

b) $2\frac{1}{9} - \frac{5}{9} = \boxed{}\ \dfrac{\boxed{}}{\boxed{}}$

4 Work out these calculations.

a) $3\frac{2}{5} - \frac{4}{5} = \boxed{}\ \dfrac{\boxed{}}{\boxed{}}$

b) $3\frac{1}{3} - \frac{2}{3} = \boxed{}\ \dfrac{\boxed{}}{\boxed{}}$

c) $1\frac{5}{8} - \frac{7}{8} = \dfrac{\boxed{}}{\boxed{}}$

d) $3\frac{2}{8} - \frac{5}{8} = \boxed{}\ \dfrac{\boxed{}}{\boxed{}}$

e) $7\frac{5}{12} - \frac{11}{12} = \boxed{}\ \dfrac{\boxed{}}{\boxed{}}$

f) $\boxed{}\ \dfrac{\boxed{}}{\boxed{}} - \frac{7}{10} = 3\frac{5}{10}$

g) $\boxed{}\ \frac{1}{8} - \frac{5}{8} = 4\dfrac{\boxed{}}{8}$

h) $7\frac{1}{5} - \dfrac{\boxed{}}{\boxed{}} = 6\frac{3}{5}$

5 $2\frac{9}{11} - \frac{3}{11} - \frac{9}{11} = \boxed{}\frac{\boxed{}}{\boxed{}}$

I will do the subtractions in a different order to make this easier to work out.

6 Millie has $2\frac{5}{7}$ litres of juice. Each day Millie drinks $\frac{6}{7}$ of a litre of juice.

CHALLENGE

a) How many days will the juice last?

Millie has enough juice for $\boxed{}$ days.

b) How much juice is left over?

There is $\frac{\boxed{}}{\boxed{}}$ of a litre of juice left over.

Reflect

Draw a diagram to help you explain the answer to $2\frac{1}{5} - \frac{3}{5}$.

114

Subtract from whole amounts

1 Amelia has 2 cakes. She eats $\frac{3}{8}$ of one of the cakes with her friend.

How much cake does she have left?

 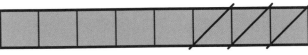

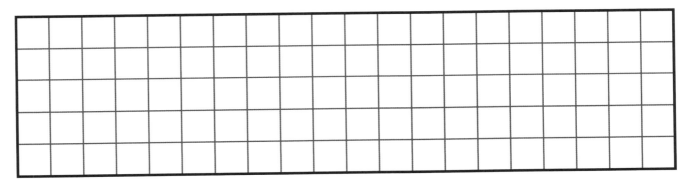

2 Complete the following calculations. Use the fraction strips to help you.

a) $3 - \frac{1}{5} = \boxed{} \frac{\boxed{}}{\boxed{}}$

b) $3 - \frac{2}{5} = \boxed{} \frac{\boxed{}}{\boxed{}}$

c) $3 - \frac{3}{5} = \boxed{} \frac{\boxed{}}{\boxed{}}$

d) $3 - \frac{4}{5} = \boxed{} \frac{\boxed{}}{\boxed{}}$

e) $3 - \frac{5}{5} = \boxed{} \frac{\boxed{}}{\boxed{}}$

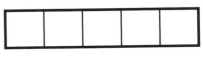

→ Textbook 4B p156

3 **a)** What is $3 - \frac{4}{7}$?

$$3 - \frac{4}{7} = \frac{\boxed{}}{\boxed{}}$$

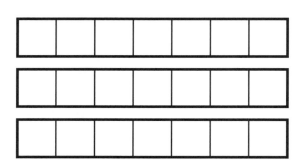

b) Mary says that $5 - \frac{2}{7} = \frac{3}{7}$.

What mistake has Mary made? Explain what the correct answer should be.

_____

_____

_____

4 Work out the following calculations.

a) $4 - \frac{6}{9} = \frac{\boxed{}}{\boxed{}}$ $4 - \frac{7}{9} = \frac{\boxed{}}{\boxed{}}$ $4 - \frac{8}{9} = \frac{\boxed{}}{\boxed{}}$

b) $5 - \frac{6}{9} = \frac{\boxed{}}{\boxed{}}$ $5 - \frac{7}{9} = \frac{\boxed{}}{\boxed{}}$ $5 - \frac{8}{9} = \frac{\boxed{}}{\boxed{}}$

c) $10 - \frac{2}{3} = \frac{\boxed{}}{\boxed{}}$ $8 - \frac{2}{3} = \frac{\boxed{}}{\boxed{}}$ $6 - \frac{2}{3} = \frac{\boxed{}}{\boxed{}}$

d) $6 - \frac{3}{4} = \frac{\boxed{}}{\boxed{}}$ $6 - \frac{4}{5} = \frac{\boxed{}}{\boxed{}}$ $6 - \frac{9}{10} = \frac{\boxed{}}{\boxed{}}$

5 Complete the calculations.

a) $5 - \dfrac{\boxed{}}{\boxed{}} = 4\dfrac{3}{7}$

b) $1 - \dfrac{\boxed{}}{\boxed{}} = \dfrac{1}{3}$

c) $16 - \dfrac{2}{9} = \boxed{} \dfrac{\boxed{}}{\boxed{}}$

d) $10 - \dfrac{\boxed{}}{\boxed{}} = 9\dfrac{1}{3}$

e) $\boxed{} - \dfrac{2}{5} = 4\dfrac{3}{5}$

f) $\boxed{} - \dfrac{1}{4} = 9\dfrac{3}{4}$

6 Jen is going to run 5 km. She runs $\dfrac{5}{8}$ km every 10 minutes.

Will she complete the run in less than 1 hour?

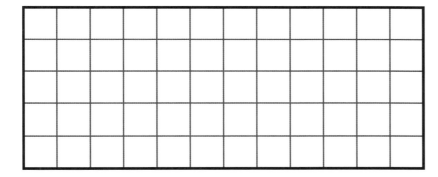

CHALLENGE

I remember there are 60 minutes in 1 hour.

Reflect

$4 - \dfrac{2}{9} = \dfrac{1}{4}$

Is this calculation correct? Draw diagrams to explain your reasoning.

Date: _____

Problem solving – add and subtract fractions ❶

1 There is 3 kg of flour in a cupboard.

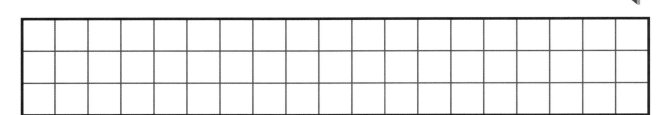

a) Holly uses $\frac{5}{7}$ kg to make bread. How much flour is left in the cupboard?

There is [ ] $\frac{\square}{\square}$ kg of flour left in the cupboard.

b) Tulpesh uses $\frac{6}{7}$ kg more flour than Holly to make bread. How much flour does he use?

Tulpesh uses $\frac{\square}{\square}$ kg of flour.

c) How much flour is used by Holly and Tulpesh in total?

$\frac{\square}{\square}$ kg of flour is used in total.

2 A farmer ploughed $\frac{5}{7}$ of an acre of his field in the morning and $\frac{4}{7}$ of an acre in the afternoon.

> An acre is a measure of land.

How much of his field did the farmer plough in total?

The farmer ploughed ⬚⬚ acres of his field in total.

3 Abigail, Phoebe and Naomi have a bottle of juice.

Abigail drinks $\frac{3}{17}$ of the bottle.

Phoebe drinks $\frac{2}{17}$ more than Abigail.

What fraction of the juice is remaining for Naomi?

> First, I am going to find out how much Phoebe drinks and then how much Abigail and Phoebe drink altogether.

⬚⬚ of the juice is remaining.

4 Fill in the empty boxes.

I can see three different ways.
I wonder if there are more.

$$\frac{\boxed{}}{8} + \frac{\boxed{}}{8} - \frac{\boxed{}}{8} = \frac{7}{8}$$

How many ways can you find to complete it?

5 Axel picked $\frac{1}{3}$ kg of strawberries and Catherine picked $\frac{2}{3}$ kg of strawberries.

CHALLENGE

Esme ate $\frac{3}{7}$ kg of the strawberries collected. What amount of strawberries were left?

$\dfrac{\boxed{}}{\boxed{}}$ kg of strawberries were left.

Reflect

Discuss with a partner about how you solved one of the problems today.

Problem solving – add and subtract fractions ❷

1 Mo and Amelia each order an omelette.

Mo eats $\frac{5}{8}$ of his omelette.

Amelia eats $\frac{7}{8}$ of her omelette.

What fraction has been eaten in total?

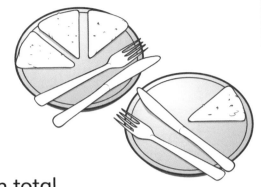

$\dfrac{\boxed{}}{\boxed{}}$ of the omelettes have been eaten in total.

2 The answer to each of the following questions is $\frac{7}{5}$.

Complete the questions.

a) $\dfrac{9}{5} - \dfrac{\boxed{}}{5} = \dfrac{7}{5}$

b) $\dfrac{3}{5} + \dfrac{\boxed{}}{5} = \dfrac{7}{5}$

c) $\dfrac{1}{5} + \dfrac{1}{5} + \dfrac{\boxed{}}{5} = \dfrac{7}{5}$

d) $1 + \dfrac{\boxed{}}{5} = \dfrac{7}{5}$

e) $\dfrac{10}{5} - \dfrac{\boxed{}}{5} = \dfrac{7}{5}$

f) $2 - \dfrac{\boxed{}}{5} = \dfrac{7}{5}$

g) $2 - \dfrac{1}{5} - \dfrac{\boxed{}}{5} = \dfrac{7}{5}$

h) $\dfrac{3}{5} + \dfrac{3}{5} + \dfrac{\boxed{}}{5} = \dfrac{7}{5}$

3 Use the number lines to help you complete the following calculations.

a) $\dfrac{5}{6} + \dfrac{3}{6} - \dfrac{4}{6} = \dfrac{\boxed{}}{6}$

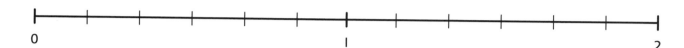

b) $\dfrac{7}{9} - \dfrac{5}{9} + \dfrac{8}{9} = \dfrac{\boxed{}}{9}$

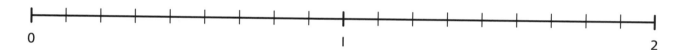

c) $1 + \dfrac{3}{5} + \dfrac{2}{5} - \dfrac{8}{5} = \dfrac{\boxed{}}{5}$

4 Three jars contain $\frac{3}{8}$ kg, $\frac{7}{8}$ kg and $\frac{7}{8}$ kg of coffee.

Each jar can hold a total of 1 kg.

How many full jars of coffee can be made using the coffee?

Show all your working.

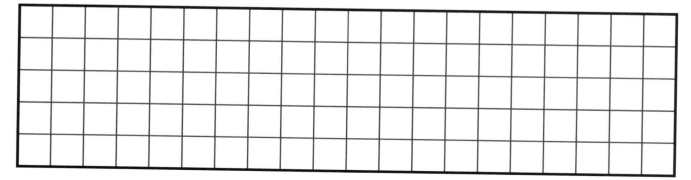

5 Florence and Kofi are running a race.

Florence runs 3 km in total. Kofi runs $\frac{3}{4}$ km in total.

How much further does Florence run than Kofi?
Give your answer as a mixed number.

> I will use a fraction strip to help me.

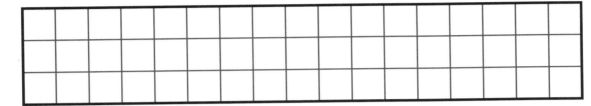

Florence runs ☐ $\frac{\square}{\square}$ km more than Kofi.

CHALLENGE

6 Work out the following calculations.

a) $\frac{3}{6} + \frac{2}{5} + \frac{3}{6} + \frac{3}{5} = \boxed{}$

b) $\frac{4}{7} + \frac{3}{8} + \frac{5}{8} + \frac{3}{7} = \boxed{}$

c) $\frac{4}{5} + \frac{1}{5} - \frac{2}{3} = \boxed{}$

Reflect

The answer is $\frac{17}{10}$. What was the question? Create your own calculation.

Date: _____

Fraction of an amount

1 Emily has three different-sized teddy bears – a small teddy bear, a medium teddy bear and a large teddy bear.

The large teddy bear is 42 cm tall.

a) The small teddy bear is $\frac{1}{7}$ the height of the large teddy bear.

How tall is the small teddy bear?

◻ ÷ ◻ = ◻

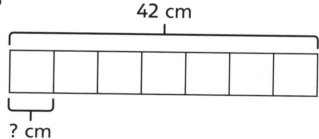

42 cm

? cm

The small teddy bear is ◻ cm tall.

b) The medium teddy bear is $\frac{4}{7}$ the height of the large teddy bear.

How tall is the medium teddy bear?

◻ ÷ ◻ = ◻

◻ × ◻ = ◻

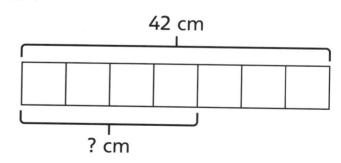

42 cm

? cm

The medium teddy bear is ◻ cm tall.

2 Complete each question.

a) $\frac{1}{3}$ of 30 m = ☐ m

b) $\frac{2}{3}$ of 27 kg = ☐ kg

c) $\frac{5}{6}$ of £18 = £ ☐

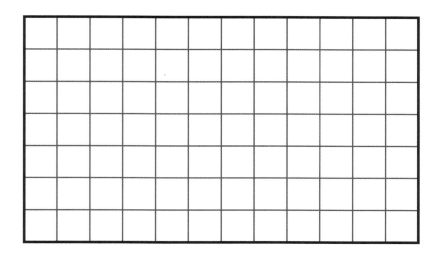

3 Is this statement true or false?

$\frac{3}{8}$ of 24 = $\frac{1}{4}$ of 36

Show your working out and circle your answer.

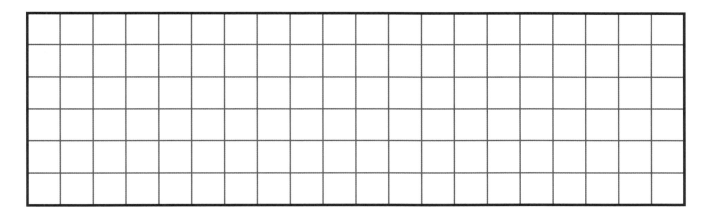

4 Match each calculation to the correct answer.

$\frac{2}{3}$ of 18		15
$\frac{1}{9}$ of 18		7
$\frac{5}{6}$ of 18		2
$\frac{7}{18}$ of 18		12

125

5 Complete the following calculations.

a) $\frac{1}{3}$ of ⬚ = 2

c) $\frac{1}{⬚}$ of 70 kg = 10 kg

b) $\frac{1}{5}$ of ⬚ = 8

d) $\frac{⬚}{⬚}$ of 42 = 35

6 Chloe got $\frac{5}{7}$ of her test correct.

Mike got $\frac{3}{8}$ of the same test incorrect.

The test was out of 56 marks.

Who got more marks and by how many?

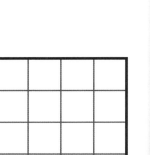
CHALLENGE

Reflect

Write a question that could go with this diagram.

45 cm

? cm

Problem solving – fraction of an amount

1 Which is greater $\frac{1}{3}$ of 18, or $\frac{2}{9}$ of 36?

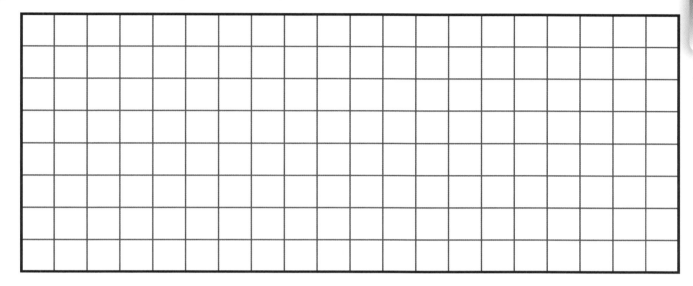

_____ is greater.

2 Work out the missing values in these fraction strips.

a)

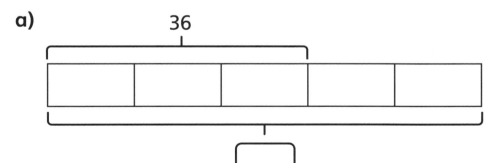

b)

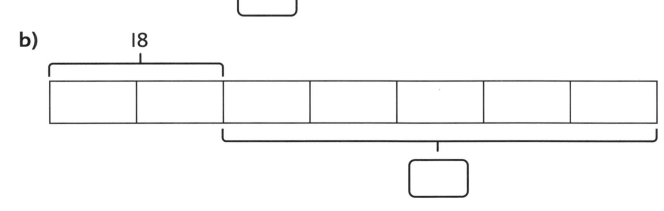

3 **a)** Mary has 16 cubes.

$\frac{1}{8}$ of the cubes are red.

$\frac{3}{8}$ of the cubes are blue.

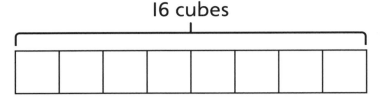

16 cubes

The rest of the cubes are yellow.

How many of each colour cube are there?

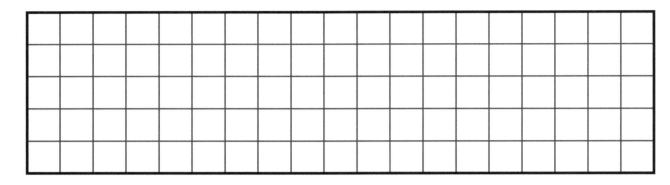

Red = ☐   Blue = ☐   Yellow = ☐

b) Gino has 40 pencils.

$\frac{3}{5}$ of the pencils are red.

$\frac{3}{8}$ of the remaining pencils are blue.

The rest are green.

How many of each coloured pencil are there?

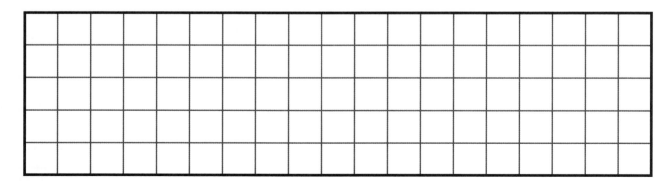

Red = ☐   Blue = ☐   Green = ☐

4 Cailyn uses 18 place value counters to make a number.

$\frac{1}{6}$ of the counters are 100s.

$\frac{4}{9}$ of the counters are 10s.

The rest of the counters are 1s.

What number has Cailyn made?

Cailyn has made the number ⬚.

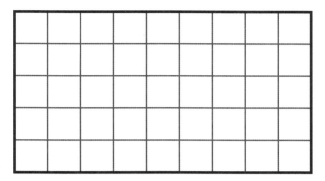

5 Find the missing numbers.

CHALLENGE

a) $\frac{3}{5}$ of 40 = $\frac{2}{3}$ of ⬚

b) $\frac{3}{5}$ of 40 = $\frac{2}{\boxed{}}$ of 60

Reflect

$\frac{2}{3}$ of a number is 18.

Eva thinks that the number is 12 because 18 ÷ 3 = 6 and then 6 × 2 = 12.

Explain Eva's mistake.

Date: _____

End of unit check

My journal

1 Explain the following equivalences. Use the number line to help you.

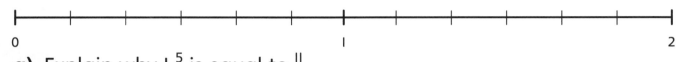

0   1   2

a) Explain why $1\frac{5}{6}$ is equal to $\frac{11}{6}$.

_____

_____

b) Explain why $\frac{5}{6} + \frac{3}{6}$ is equal to $1\frac{2}{6}$.

_____

_____

c) Explain why $2 - \frac{5}{6}$ is equal to $1\frac{1}{6}$.

_____

_____

Power check

How do you feel about your work in this unit?

Power puzzle

Holly is sharing some grapes with 4 children: Emma, Andy, Reena and Lee.

- Holly has 48 grapes.

- She gives $\frac{1}{6}$ of the grapes to Emma.

- She then eats 1 of the grapes that she has left.

- Holly then gives $\frac{1}{3}$ of the remaining grapes to Andy.

- Holly then eats 2 of the grapes she has left.

- She then gives $\frac{3}{8}$ of the remaining grapes to Reena.

- Holly then eats 3 of the grapes that are left.

- Holly finally gives Lee $\frac{3}{4}$ of the grapes she has remaining.

- Holly eats the grapes that she has left.

How many grapes does Holly eat in total?

Who gets the most grapes?

Create your own story like this and then swap with a partner.

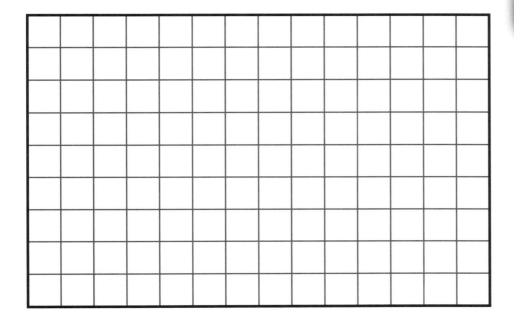

Date: _____

Tenths as fractions

1 What fraction of each grid is shaded?

a)
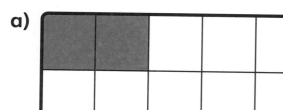

b)
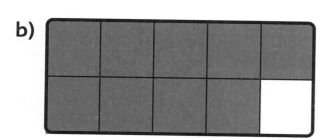

2 **a)** What fraction of the cubes are grey?

b) What fraction of the beads are grey?

↑ Textbook 4B p180

3 What fractions are shown in these representations?

a)

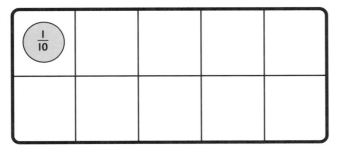

b)

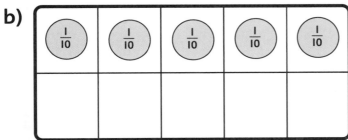

4 Shade in $\frac{7}{10}$ of each shape.

a)

b)

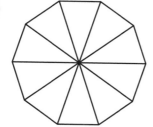

c)

5 Annie says $\frac{3}{10}$ of this shape is shaded.

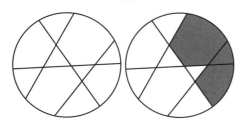

Is Annie correct? Explain your answer.

_____

_____

6 Shade in $\frac{1}{10}$ of each shape.

a)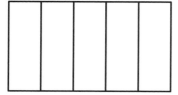

b)

Reflect

How many tenths are there in a whole?

Explain how you know this below.

_____

_____

_____

Date: _____

Tenths as decimals

1 What decimals are represented on each of these ten frames?

a)

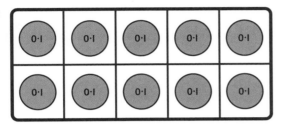

b)

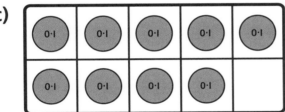

c)

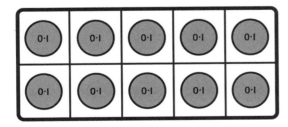

2 Danny has made a number on a ten frame.

Danny says he has made the number 0·10.

a) Explain to a partner why Danny is wrong.

b) What number has Danny made?

3 Draw counters to represent the following decimals.

a) 0·3

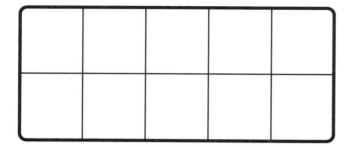

b) 0·6

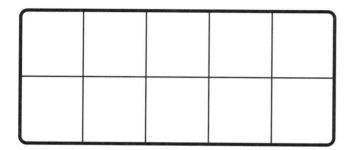

4 Complete the sentences.

a)

The white cubes represent [ ] of the whole.

b)

The white beads represent [ ] of the whole.

5 Shade in 0·2 of each shape.

CHALLENGE

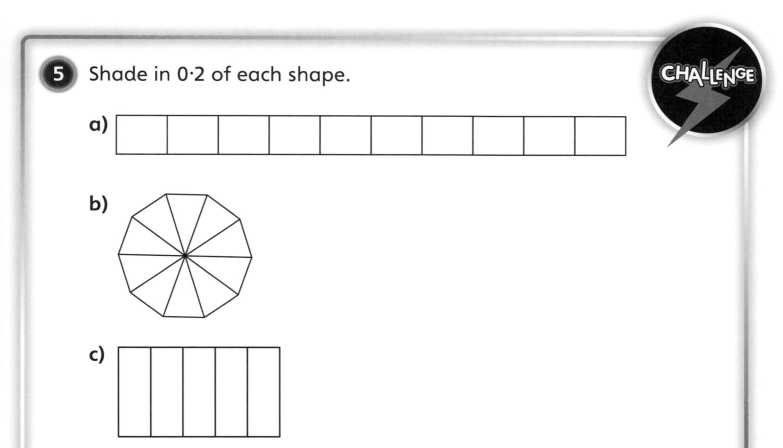

a)

b)

c)

Reflect

Show that $\frac{2}{10}$ is the same as 0·2.

Date: _____

Tenths on a place value grid

1 What numbers are represented here?

a)
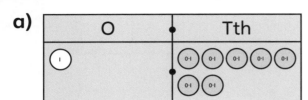

b)
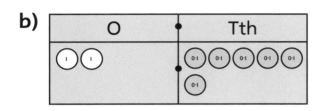

2 Look at the representations below. Complete the sentences.

a)
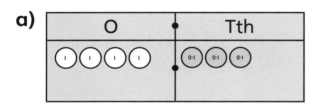

The number ⬚ has ⬚ ones and ⬚ tenths.

b)
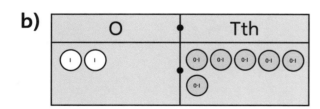

The number ⬚ has ⬚ ones and ⬚ tenths.

138

3 Draw counters to represent the following decimals.

a) 3·5

O	Tth

b) 42·6

T	O	Tth

4 Filip has made this number.

T	O	Tth
10 10 10 10		0·1 0·1 0·1 0·1 0·1 0·1

Filip says this is the number 4·6.

a) Explain to a partner why Filip is wrong.

b) What number has Filip made?

5 What is the value of the 7 in each of these numbers?

a) 3·7 _____

b) 24·7 _____

c) 73·5 _____

139

6 Match each statement to the correct number.

This number has 7 tenths.

74·5

The digit in the tenths column is I more than the digit in the ones column.

7·6

There are more ones than tenths.

0·7

7 Olivia is making decimals using these digit cards.

CHALLENGE

6 7 2 8

She uses three of the cards like this ☐☐·☐

a) What is the largest decimal she can make?

b) What is the smallest decimal she can make?

Reflect

Make the numbers 3·5 and 17·5 on a place value grid. Discuss with a partner what is the same and what is different about the numbers.

Date: _____

Tenths on a number line

↓ Textbook 4B p192

1 Complete the number lines.

a)

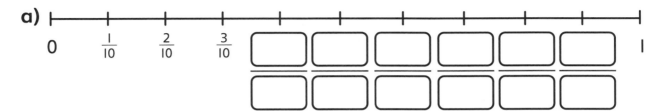

0    $\frac{1}{10}$ $\frac{2}{10}$ $\frac{3}{10}$ ☐ ☐ ☐ ☐ ☐ ☐   1

☐ ☐ ☐ ☐ ☐

b)

0   0·1   ☐ ☐   0·4   ☐ ☐   0·7   0·8   ☐ ☐

c)

2   2·1   ☐   2·3   ☐   2·5   2·6   ☐   2·8   ☐   3

2 What numbers are marked by the arrows?

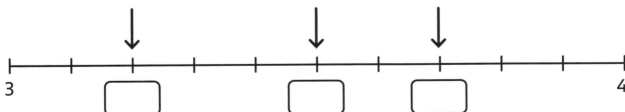

3   ☐   ☐   ☐   4

141

3 Draw lines to where each number should go on the number line.

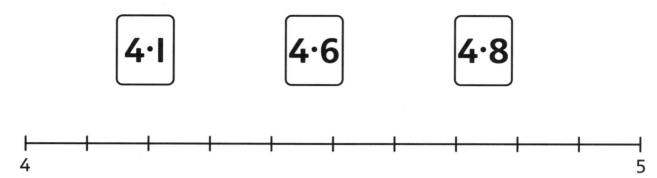

```
|----|----|----|----|----|----|----|----|----|----|
4                                                  5
```

4 Ambika is counting up in 0·1s from 2·4.

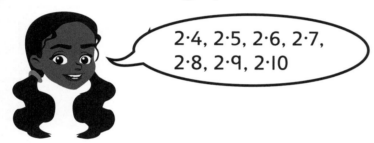

2·4, 2·5, 2·6, 2·7, 2·8, 2·9, 2·10

What mistake has Ambika made?

_____

_____

5 Complete the number track.

4·5	4·6	4·7				

6 Complete the bottom scale to show the decimal equivalent of each fraction.

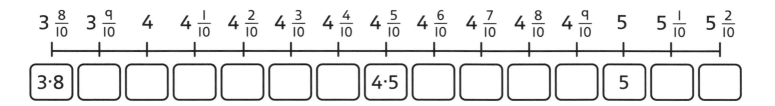

$3\frac{8}{10}$ $3\frac{9}{10}$ 4 $4\frac{1}{10}$ $4\frac{2}{10}$ $4\frac{3}{10}$ $4\frac{4}{10}$ $4\frac{5}{10}$ $4\frac{6}{10}$ $4\frac{7}{10}$ $4\frac{8}{10}$ $4\frac{9}{10}$ 5 $5\frac{1}{10}$ $5\frac{2}{10}$

3·8 | | | | | | | 4·5 | | | | | 5 | | |

7 Record the position of the following numbers on the number line below.

CHALLENGE

3·9 $4\frac{1}{2}$ 4·6   5·0

4·3

Reflect

Discuss with a partner the mistake that has been made in the number line below. Then rewrite the number line correctly.

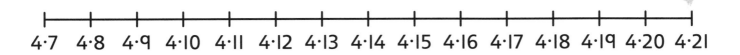

4·7   4·8   4·9   4·10   4·11   4·12   4·13   4·14   4·15   4·16   4·17   4·18   4·19   4·20   4·21

Date: _____

Tenths on a number line ❷

1 Draw an arrow to where each number is on the number line.

a) 0·6

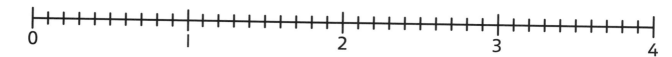

b) 1·6

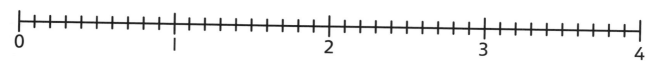

c) 2·6

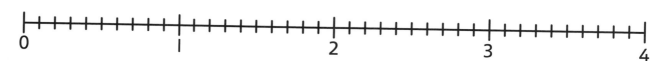

d) 3·6

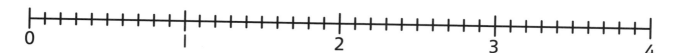

2 What are the numbers marked by the arrows?

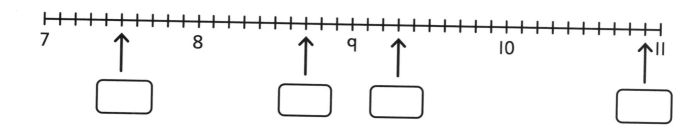

144

3 What is the length of each bug?

a)

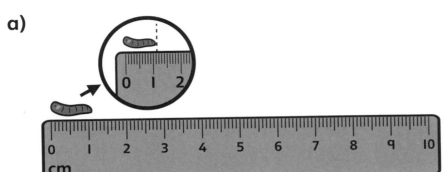

The worm is ⬜ cm long.

b)

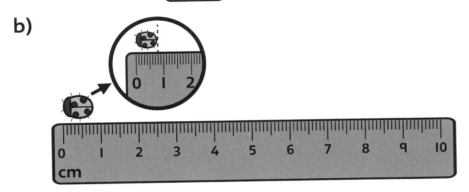

The ladybird is ⬜ cm long.

4 How much water is in each of the containers?

a)

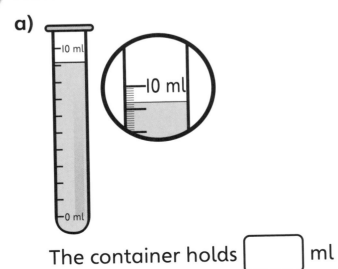

The container holds ⬜ ml of water.

b)

The container holds ⬜ ml of water.

5 **a)** How long is the grasshopper?

The grasshopper is ☐ cm long.

CHALLENGE

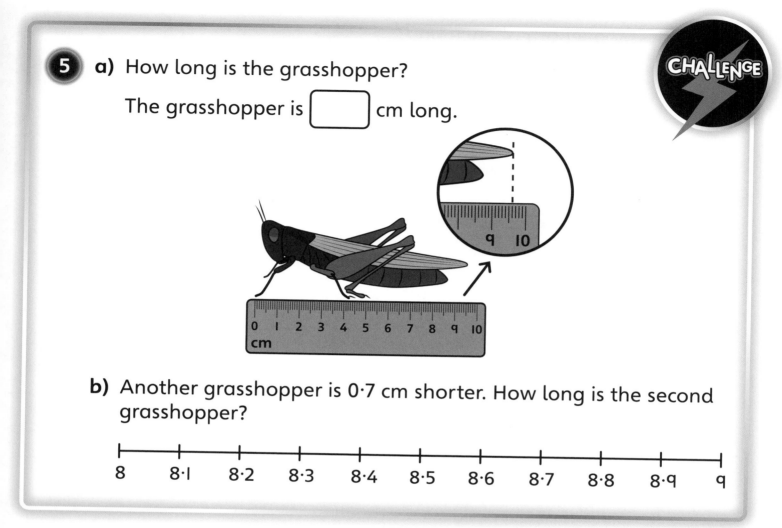

b) Another grasshopper is 0·7 cm shorter. How long is the second grasshopper?

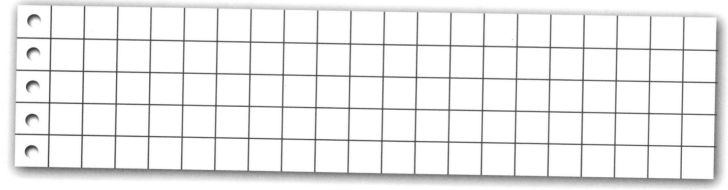

8   8·1   8·2   8·3   8·4   8·5   8·6   8·7   8·8   8·9   9

Reflect

Use a ruler to measure three objects in your classroom.

Give your answers as decimals.

Divide 1 digit by 10

1 Ebo is dividing 3 by 10.

He makes the number on a place value grid.

O		Tth
① ① ①	•	

He exchanges each counter for 10 tenths.

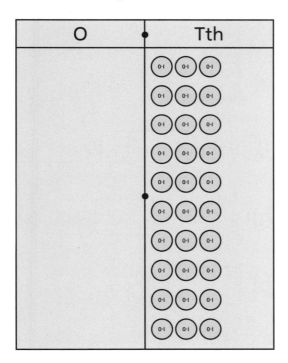

O		Tth

Use Ebo's method to work out 3 ÷ 10 = ☐.

2 Work out these calculations.

a) 4 ÷ 10 = ☐

c) 9 ÷ 10 = ☐

b) 7 ÷ 10 = ☐

d) 2 ÷ 10 = ☐

147

3 Complete the bar models.

a)

5								

b)

6								

4 Complete the following calculations.

a) $6 \div 10 = 0.\boxed{}$

b) $8 \div \boxed{} = 0.8$

c) $1 \div 10 = \boxed{}$

d) $0 \div 10 = \boxed{}$

e) $\boxed{} \div 10 = 0.4$

f) $0.5 = \boxed{} \div 10$

g) $0.3 = 3 \div \boxed{}$

h) $\boxed{} \div 10 = 1$

5 Max says, 'I divided by 10 is equal to 10 tenths'.

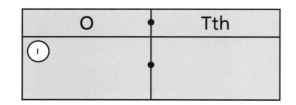
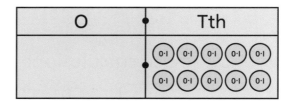

Discuss Max's mistake with a partner.

6 Do you agree or disagree with the following calculation?

$$5 \div 10 = 2$$

I agree / disagree because _____

_____

_____ .

7 What patterns can you spot in the following calculations?

$1 \div 10 = 0{\cdot}1$

$2 \div 10 = 0{\cdot}2$

$3 \div 10 = 0{\cdot}3$

I notice that _____

_____

_____ .

Reflect

Explain how to divide a 1-digit number by 10.

_____

_____

Date: _____

Divide 2 digits by 10

1 Andy is dividing 13 by 10.

T	O	•	Tth
⑩	① ① ①	•	

a) Discuss with a partner a method Andy could use.

b) What is 13 ÷ 10? ☐

c) Describe what happens to each of the digits when you divide by 10.

_____

_____

2 Complete the following calculations.

a) 15 ÷ 10 = ☐

b) 19 ÷ 10 = ☐

c) 25 ÷ 10 = ☐

d) 50 ÷ 10 = ☐

e) 93 ÷ 10 = ☐

f) 7 ÷ 10 = ☐

g) 19 ÷ 10 = ☐

h) 38 ÷ 10 = ☐

i) 77 ÷ 10 = ☐

j) 100 ÷ 10 = ☐

3 Complete the bar model.

76								

4 Reena has a 28 metre long rope.

She cuts it into 10 equal length pieces.

How long is each piece of rope? ☐ m

5 Are the following calculations true or false? Circle your answer.

$43 \div 10 = 3·4$ True / False

$10 \div 43 = 4·3$ True / False

$43 \div 10 = 4·3$ True / False

$4·3 = 43 \div 10$ True / False

6 Complete the following calculations.

a) ☐ $\div 10 = 6·4$

b) ☐ $\div 10 = 1·8$

c) ☐ $\div 10 = 7·2$

d) $4·4 = 44 \div$ ☐

e) ☐ $\div 10 = 3·9$

f) $6·5 =$ ☐ $\div 10$

7 Is the following statement always, sometimes or never true? Provide examples to support your answer.

'A 2-digit number divided by 10 will always have an answer with a digit in the tenths column.'

Always true   Sometimes true   Never true

8 How many different ways is it possible to complete the following using a 2-digit number?

CHALLENGE

$7.9 > \boxed{} \div 10 > 7.3$

$\boxed{}$ ways

Reflect

What is the same and what is different about dividing a 1-digit number by 10 and dividing a 2-digit number by 10?

Hundredths as fractions

1 Write each representation as a fraction.

a)

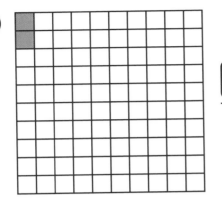

$\dfrac{}{100}$

c)

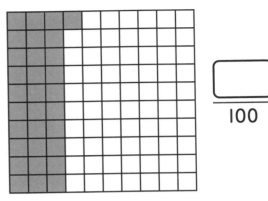

$\dfrac{}{100}$

b)

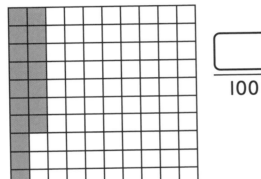

$\dfrac{}{100}$

d)

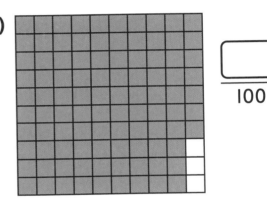

$\dfrac{}{100}$

2 Represent each fraction on the grid.

a) $\dfrac{14}{100}$

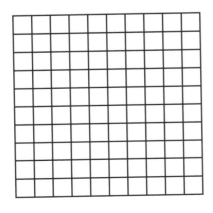

b) $\dfrac{30}{100}$

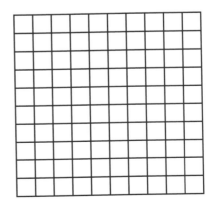

3 What fractions are represented by the counters?

a)

$$\frac{\boxed{}}{100}$$

b)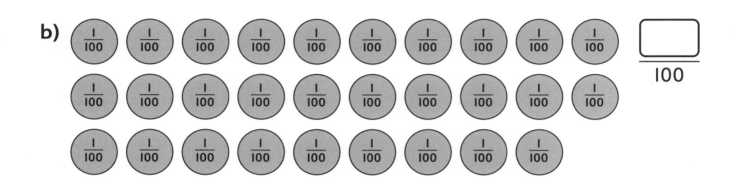

$$\frac{\boxed{}}{100}$$

4 What fraction of the grid is shaded?

Write your answer in two ways.

$$\frac{\boxed{}}{100} \text{ and } \frac{\boxed{}}{10}$$

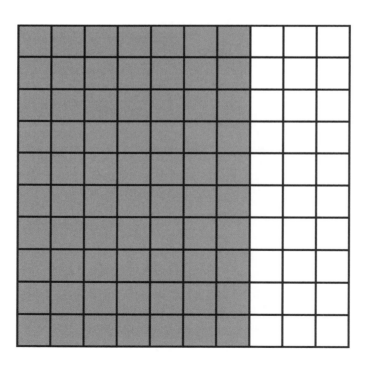

5 Here is a hundredths grid.

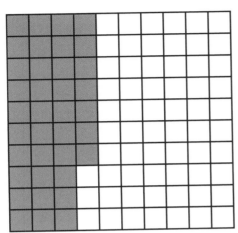

I think this shows $\frac{37}{100}$.

I think this shows $\frac{3}{10} + \frac{7}{100}$.

a) Explain to a partner why each person is correct.

b) On this grid represent $\frac{5}{10} + \frac{3}{100}$.

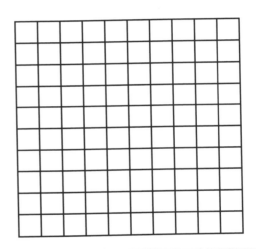

Reflect

What can you see?

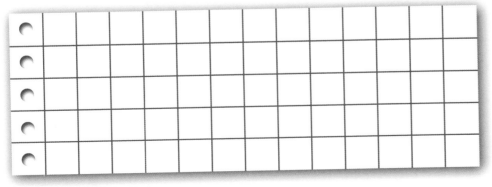

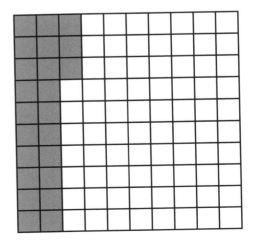

Date: _____

Hundredths as decimals

1 Write each representation as a decimal.

a)

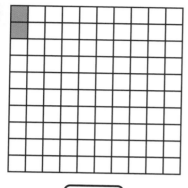

☐

c)

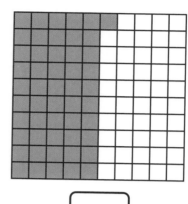

☐

b)

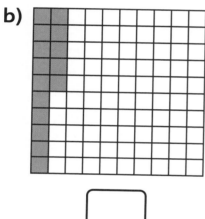

☐

d)

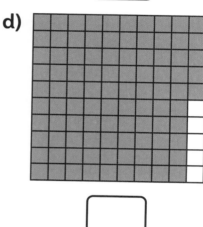

☐

2 Represent each decimal on the grid.

a) 0·07

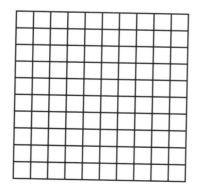

b) 0·28

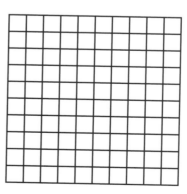

↑ Textbook 4B p212

3 What decimal is represented here?

0·01 0·01 0·01 0·01 0·01 0·01 0·01 0·01 0·01 0·01 0·01

4 Complete the table.

Fraction	$\frac{16}{100}$	$\frac{18}{100}$		$\frac{22}{100}$	
Decimal	0·16		0·20		

5 Complete these equivalent fractions and decimals.

a) $\frac{32}{100} = \boxed{}$

b) $0·27 = \dfrac{\boxed{}}{100}$

c) $0·39 = \dfrac{\boxed{}}{\boxed{}}$

d) Nineteen hundredths = $\boxed{}$

e) $0·46 = \boxed{}$ hundredths

f) $\dfrac{\boxed{}}{100} = 0·52$

g) $0·59 = \dfrac{\boxed{}}{\boxed{}}$

h) $\dfrac{\boxed{}}{\boxed{}} = 0·93$

i) Ninety hundredths = $\boxed{}$

j) $0·03 = \boxed{}$ hundredths

6 Luis writes the number of shaded squares as 0·5 of the hundredths grid.

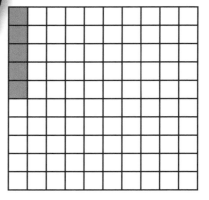

Do you agree or disagree with Luis?

I agree / disagree because _____

_____

_____ .

7 Mo, Isla and Zac have shared 100 counters between them.

Use the bar model to calculate what fraction of the whole each child has. Record this as a decimal.

100		
Isla 45	Mo 23	Zac ?

Mo has $\dfrac{\boxed{}}{100}$, or $\boxed{}$

Isla has $\dfrac{\boxed{}}{100}$, or $\boxed{}$

Zac has $\dfrac{\boxed{}}{100}$, or $\boxed{}$

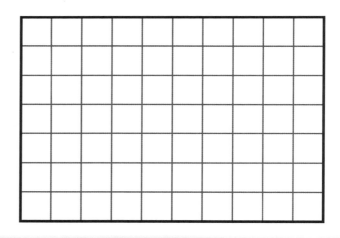

Reflect

Represent 0·35 in different ways.

Date: _____

Hundredths on a place value grid

1 What numbers are shown?

a)

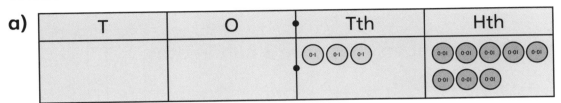

T	O	Tth	Hth
		0·1 0·1 0·1	0·01 0·01 0·01 0·01 0·01 0·01 0·01 0·01

☐

b)

T	O	Tth	Hth
		0·1 0·1 0·1 0·1 0·1 0·1 0·1	0·01 0·01

☐

c)

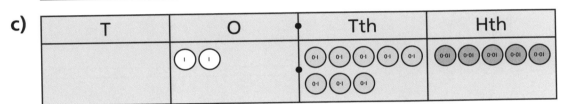

T	O	Tth	Hth
	1 1	0·1 0·1 0·1 0·1 0·1 0·1 0·1 0·1	0·01 0·01 0·01 0·01 0·01

☐

d)

T	O	Tth	Hth
	1 1		0·01 0·01 0·01

☐

e)

T	O	Tth	Hth
10	1 1 1	0·1 0·1 0·1 0·1 0·1 0·1 0·1 0·1	

☐

f)

T	O	Tth	Hth
10	1 1 1	0·1 0·1 0·1 0·1 0·1 0·1 0·1 0·1	0·01 0·01 0·01 0·01 0·01

☐

2 Draw counters to represent the number 1·35.

T	O	Tth	Hth

3 **a)** Circle all the numbers that have 5 tenths.

     0·57   1·75   5·32   52·19   7·58

   b) Circle all the numbers that have 3 hundredths.

     1·32   0·03   7·13   13·08   9·33

4 What is the value of the digit that is underlined?

   a) 1·7̲6 _____

   b) 3·6̲2̲ _____

   c) 1̲2·95 _____

5 Complete the following part-whole models.

   a)

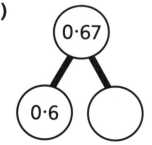

   b)

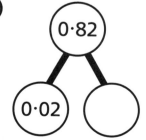

   c)

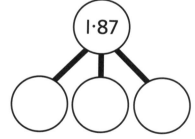

   d)

6 Complete these partitions.

a) 6·18 = 6 + 0·1 + ☐

b) 1·59 = 1 + ☐ + ☐

c) ☐ = 5 + 0·6 + 0·01

d) ☐ = 7 + 0·03

e) ☐ = 7 + 0·03 + 0·8

7 Lee has the following place value counters. He adds them to a place value grid one by one. What number is represented after each counter is added?

Reflect

Tell a partner three things you know about the number 8·45.

Date: _____

Divide 1 or 2 digits by 100

1 Here are five hundredths grids.

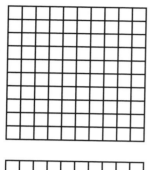 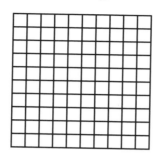 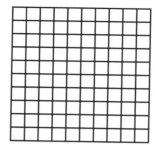

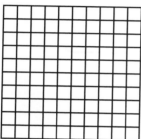 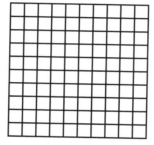

a) Shade in $\frac{1}{100}$ of each square.

b) What is $5 \div 100$? ☐

2 Aki is dividing 15 by 100.

I have noticed that when you divide by 100 the digits move columns.

T	O	Tth	Hth
1	5		

Explain what happens to the digits when you divide by 100.

_____

_____

3   Work out these calculations.

a) $9 \div 100 =$ ☐

b) $12 \div 100 =$ ☐

c) $17 \div 100 =$ ☐

d) $28 \div 100 =$ ☐

e) $35 \div 100 =$ ☐

f) $42 \div 100 =$ ☐

g) $7 \div 100 =$ ☐

h) $70 \div 100 =$ ☐

i) $83 \div 100 =$ ☐

j) $99 \div 100 =$ ☐

4   A barrel contains 48 litres of water.

The water is shared equally between 100 buckets.

How much water is in each bucket? ☐ litres

5   Work out the missing numbers.

a)   ☐ $\div 100 = 0.02$

b)   ☐ $\div 100 = 0.38$

c)   ☐ $\div 100 = 0.6$

d) $33 \div$ ☐ $= 0.33$

6 Are the following statements true or false? Write your answer in the table.

When you divide by 100...	True or False?
The digits change.	
Any digit in the ones column moves to the tenths column.	
Any digit in the tens column moves to the tenths column.	
Each digit becomes $\frac{1}{100}$ of the value.	

7 **a)** If I divide 45 by 100, what will the value of the digit 5 be in the answer?   **CHALLENGE**

The value of the digit 5 in the answer is _____ .

b) If I find $\frac{1}{100}$ of 59, what will the value of the digit 9 be in the answer?

The value of the digit 9 in the answer is _____ .

Reflect

Explain how knowing $\frac{12}{100} = 0.12$ helps working out $12 \div 100$.

_____

_____

Date: _____

Divide by 10 and 100

1 Work out the following calculations.

a) $12 \div 10 = \boxed{}$ $12 \div 100 = \boxed{}$

b) $35 \div 10 = \boxed{}$ $35 \div 100 = \boxed{}$

c) $48 \div 10 = \boxed{}$ $48 \div 100 = \boxed{}$

d) $57 \div 10 = \boxed{}$ $57 \div 100 = \boxed{}$

e) $91 \div 10 = \boxed{}$ $91 \div 100 = \boxed{}$

What do you notice about the digits?

_____

_____

2 There are 10 boxes of plates.

The total mass of the boxes is 45 kg.

What is the mass of each box?

45 kg

$\boxed{}$ kg

3 What calculation does the bar model represent?

83									
8·3									

$$\boxed{} \div \boxed{} = \boxed{}$$

4 Circle the value of the <u>underlined</u> digit in 12·1<u>3</u>.

3 hundreds   3 tenths   3 ones   3 hundredths

5 Complete the following calculations.

a) $56 \div 10 = \boxed{}$

$56 \div 100 = \boxed{}$

b) $\boxed{} \div 10 = 3·4$

$\boxed{} \div 100 = 0·34$

c) $72 \div 10 = \boxed{}$

$72 \div 100 = \boxed{}$

d) $14 \div \boxed{} = 1·4$

$14 \div \boxed{} = 0·14$

6 Complete the following calculations.

a) $68 \div 10 = \boxed{}$

b) $46 \div 100 = \boxed{}$

c) $\boxed{} = 18 \div 100$

d) $4·9 = 49 \div \boxed{}$

e) $0·97 = \boxed{} \div 100$

f) $0 \div 100 = \boxed{}$

7 **a)** Danny divides a number by 10 and he gets 9·6.
What would he get if he divided his number by 100?

Explain your working.

_____

_____

b) Bella divides a number by 100 and gets 0·07. What does Bella get if she divides her number by 10?

Explain your working.

_____

_____

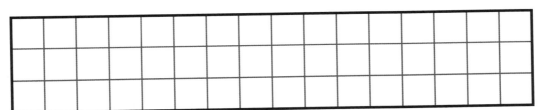

8 Prove that $\frac{1}{10}$ of 7 is equal to $\frac{1}{100}$ of 70. Show your working.

Reflect

Explain the link between dividing a number by 10 and dividing the same number by 100.

_____

_____

Date: _____

End of unit check

My journal

↑ Textbook 4B p228

1. How many different numbers can you make using the digit cards below? You must use all the cards in each number you make.

| · | 3 | 4 | 1 |

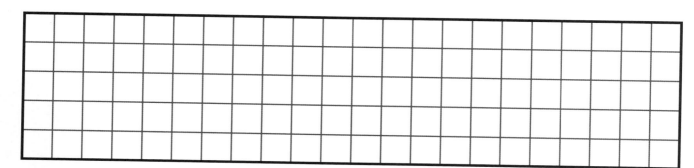

2. Choose one of the numbers you have made and represent it in as many different visual ways as possible. What is the value of these digits?

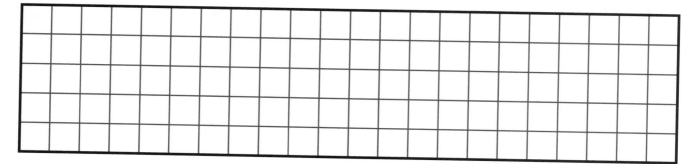

Power check

How do you feel about your work in this unit?   ?

168

Power play

- In pairs, use a spinner, like the one shown, to make a journey through the grid.

- If you move off the grid (for example, if you spin 0·1 less or 0·01 less on your first go), then you move back to (or stay on) 0·01 and it is your partner's turn.

- Who can get the furthest after 12 goes?

0·01	0·02	0·03	0·04	0·05	0·06	0·07	0·08	0·09	0·10
0·11	0·12	0·13	0·14	0·15	0·16	0·17	0·18	0·19	0·20
0·21	0·22	0·23	0·24	0·25	0·26	0·27	0·28	0·29	0·30
0·31	0·32	0·33	0·34	0·35	0·36	0·37	0·38	0·39	0·40
0·41	0·42	0·43	0·44	0·45	0·46	0·47	0·48	0·49	0·50
0·51	0·52	0·53	0·54	0·55	0·56	0·57	0·58	0·59	0·60
0·61	0·62	0·63	0·64	0·65	0·66	0·67	0·68	0·69	0·70
0·71	0·72	0·73	0·74	0·75	0·76	0·77	0·78	0·79	0·80
0·81	0·82	0·83	0·84	0·85	0·86	0·87	0·88	0·89	0·90
0·91	0·92	0·93	0·94	0·95	0·96	0·97	0·98	0·99	1·00

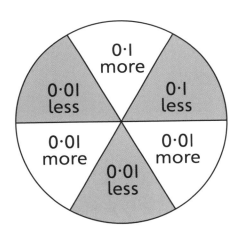

Here is an example

- Player 1 starts on 0·01.

- On their first go, player 1 spins 0·01 more, so they count on 1 hundredth and move to 0·02.

- On their second go, player 1 spins 0·1 more, so moves from 0·02 to 0·12.

My power points

Shade in the ☆ to show what you have learnt.

Shade in the ☺ if you feel happy about what you have learnt.

Unit 6

I can …

☆ ☺ Find and use factor pairs

☆ ☺ Multiply a number using written methods

☆ ☺ Find the remainder when a number is divided

☆ ☺ Choose the best way to multiply or divide

☆ ☺ Divide 2- and 3-digit numbers

Unit 7

I can …

☆ ☺ Convert between kilometres and metres

☆ ☺ Find perimeters of shapes

☆ ☺ Work out missing lengths

☆ ☺ Solve problems involving perimeter

Unit 8

I can …

☆ ☺ Understand fractions that are greater than 1

☆ ☺ Convert between mixed numbers and improper fractions

☆ ☺ Identify equivalent fractions

☆ ☺ Simplify fractions

☆ ☺ Read number lines with mixed numbers

Unit 9

I can ...

☆ ☺ Add and subtract fractions with the same denominator

☆ ☺ Subtract a fraction from a whole number

☆ ☺ Find a fraction of an amount

Unit 10

I can ...

☆ ☺ Show tenths and hundredths as a decimal

☆ ☺ Show tenths and hundredths as a fraction

☆ ☺ Show tenths and hundredths on a place value grid

☆ ☺ Divide 1- and 2-digit numbers by 10 and 100

☆ ☺ Calculate with decimals

Keep up the good work!

Notes

Notes

Squared paper

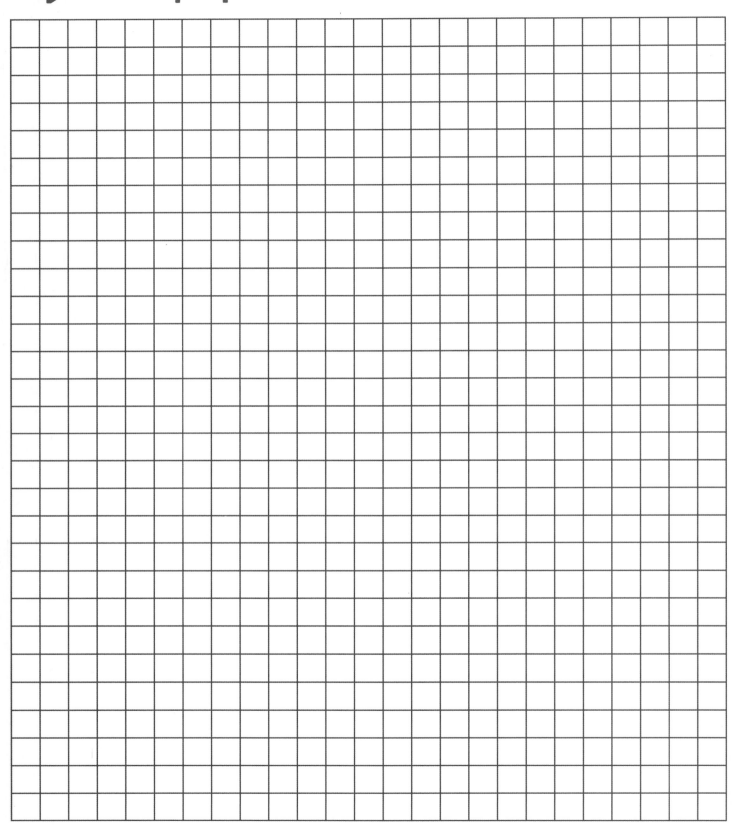